BLUEPRINT

The Comprehens
Book

Sue and Terry Dillon

Stanley Thornes (Publishers) Ltd

For Emma, Rachel and Elizabeth

First published in 1996
First published in new binding in 1997 by:
Stanley Thornes (Publishers) Ltd
Ellenborough House
Wellington Street
CHELTENHAM GL50 1YW

98 99 00 / 10 9 8 7 6 5 4 3

A catalogue record for this book is available from the British Library.

ISBN 0 7487 3454 6

Typeset by Tech-Set, Gateshead, Tyne & Wear
Printed and bound in Great Britain by
Redwood Books, Trowbridge, Wiltshire

CONTENTS

KEY to curriculum links

R.E. = Religious Education
Sc. = Science
P.S.E. = Personal and Social Education

H = History
(E) = Egyptians
(R) = Romans
(G) = Greeks
(N) = Norsemen/Vikings
(T) = Tudors
(S) = Stuarts
(V) = Victorians
(WW2) = World War II

INTRODUCTION

The Comprehension Book provides children with a wide range of fiction and non-fiction material which will encourage them to enjoy their reading and cultivate their interest in books of all kinds.

The worksheets are in approximate order of difficulty. They are intended for children from Year 2 through to Year 6 in the primary school, and may also be useful for the less able child in the secondary school.

All the activities involve the practice and development of reading skills and comprehension. At the lower levels of Key Stage 2 children are asked to practise the very basic skills of:

- interpreting a picture
- giving single-word answers to questions
- sequencing pictures or sentences
- answering simple multiple choice questions

Later worksheets cover:

- straightforward question-and-answer comprehension work
- Cloze exercises
- vocabulary development

At the higher levels of Key Stage 2 there are complex texts which demand not just the literal understanding of what has been read, but also the more advanced skills of inference and deduction. Emphasis is placed on the acquisition and application of a wide vocabulary. Some of the extracts ask children for personal responses, opinions, and the evaluation and interpretation of text.

The list of Contents indicates links with a range of National Curriculum subjects which many teachers will find invaluable. There is also a booklist which may be of interest for further reading or follow-up work.

Acknowledgements

The authors and publisher wish to express their thanks for the use of the following copyright material:

'Gilbert' from *Singing Down the Breadfruit* by Pauline Stewart published by Bodley Head, reprinted by permission of Random House Ltd; 'Latch Key' by Jackie Kay, reprinted by permission of the author, 'Dipa' by Ann Bonner, reprinted by permission of the author. Extracts from all the books listed in the Booklist on page v are reproduced by permission of Macdonald Young Books and Wayland Books.

BOOKLIST

Fiction

Title	*Author*	*Publisher*
Alice Alone	Shirley Isherwood	Macdonald Young Books
Seymour Finds a Home	Dyan Sheldon	Macdonald Young Books
Emily's Legs	Dick King-Smith	Macdonald Young Books
A Martian Comes to Stay	Penelope Lively	Macdonald Young Books
Guy Fawkes and the Gunpowder Gang	Rob Childs	Macdonald Young Books
Kijo the Baby Gorilla	Jill Jago/Gerry Livingstone	Macdonald Young Books
Sabre-tooth Sandwich	Leon Garfield	Macdonald Young Books
The Queen Cat	Ann Turnbull	Macdonald Young Books
The Excitement of being Ernest	Dick King-Smith	Macdonald Young Books
A Tickle in your Tummy	Poems chosen by Judith Elkin and Carlton Duncan	Macdonald Young Books
Ben's Big Day	Dick Cate	Macdonald Young Books
The Princess and the Parlourmaid	Jean Willis	Macdonald Young Books
Out of the Ark	Anita Ganieri	Macdonald Young Books
The Jolly Witch	Dick King-Smith	Macdonald Young Books
Mrs. Smith's Crocodile	Linda Dearsley/Frank Rodgers	Macdonald Young Books
Norse Myths	Kevin Crossley-Holland	Macdonald Young Books
Stories for Children	Oscar Wilde	Macdonald Young Books
The Dinosaur Robbers	Jeremy Strong	Macdonald Young Books
Arthur and Excalibur	Angelika Lukesch	Macdonald Young Books
Archie the Ugly Dinosaur	M. Christine Butler	Macdonald Young Books
The Magical Storyhouse	Adèle Geras	Macdonald Young Books
The Alchymist's Cat	Robin Jarvis	Macdonald Young Books
The Trouble with Mice	Pat Moore	Macdonald Young Books

Non-fiction

Title	Author	Publisher
What do we Know about the Romans?	Mike Corbishley	Macdonald Young Books
A Roman Fort	Fiona Macdonald	Macdonald Young Books
Rome in the Time of Augustus	Fiona Clarke	Macdonald Young Books
Egypt in the Time of Rameses II	Jacqueline Morley	Macdonald Young Books
An Egyptian Pyramid	Jacqueline Morley	Macdonald Young Books
What do we Know about the Egyptians?	Joanna Defrates	Macdonald Young Books
The Greek Legends	Peter Connolly	Macdonald Young Books
A Greek Temple	Fiona Macdonald	Macdonald Young Books
What do we Know about the Greeks?	Anne Pearson	Macdonald Young Books
What do we Know about the Vikings?	Hazel Mary Martell	Macdonald Young Books
Vikings and their Travels	David Salariya	Macdonald Young Books
What do we Know about the Tudors and Stuarts?	Richard Tames	Macdonald Young Books
What do we Know about the Victorians?	Richard Tames	Macdonald Young Books
The Hindu World	Patricia Bahree	Macdonald Young Books
The Sikh World	Patricia Bahree	Macdonald Young Books
The Christian World	Alan Brown	Macdonald Young Books
The Muslim World	Richard Tames	Macdonald Young Books
The Buddhist World	Anne Bancroft	Macdonald Young Books
Super Science Book of Space	Jerry Wellington	Wayland
Polar Regions	Nigel Bonner	Wayland
Pirates and Treasure	Saviour Pirotta	Wayland
Monsters of the Deep	Saviour Pirotta	Wayland

ANSWERS

Copymaster 1

1. chick
2. piglet
3. tadpole
4. kitten
5. lamb
6. calf

Copymaster 2

1. Tara likes to run.
2. Peter likes ice cream.
3. Alina likes to draw.
4. Jake likes to read.
5. Nadim likes football.
6. Ben likes to help.
7. Nicola likes to cook.
8. Amy likes to swim.

Copymaster 3

1. sandcastle
2. ice cream
3. book
4. ball
5. bucket
6. lighthouse
7. sun
8. seashell
9. sunshine
10. sandcastle
11. lighthouse

Copymaster 4

1. pram
2. lady
3. girl
4. seesaw
5. two
6. sunny
7. slide
8. smiling

Copymaster 5

Make sure the child has followed the instructions.

Copymaster 6

Make sure the child has followed the instructions.

Copymaster 7

1. I get up at 7 o'clock.
2. I wash and brush my teeth.
3. I get dressed.
4. I eat my breakfast.
5. I get ready for school.
6. Dad takes me to school.
7. I hang my coat and bag in the cloakroom.
8. I do my work.

Copymaster 8

1. stable
2. kennel
3. nest
4. sty

Copymaster 9

Check that the pictures match the text.

Copymaster 10

1. Sam looked out of his bedroom window. It had snowed in the night.
2. He washed and dressed very quickly.
3. Mum made him have a hot drink and some toast for breakfast.
4. Sam put on his anorak, scarf, hat, gloves and boots.
5. He ran out and made footprints in the snow. He was going to make a big snowman.
6. Sam made a lovely snowman. Mum put a hat and scarf on him.

Copymaster 11

1. lorry
2. train
3. motorbike
4. ambulance
5. plane
6. car
7. tractor
8. bik

Copymaster 12

2. You would go to the Post Office.
3. You would go to the bookshop.
4. The van is going to the Post Office.
5. The shoe shop is to the right of the fish shop.
6. The writing on the road says NO PARKING.
7. 3 4 6 1 5 2

Copymaster 13

1. penguin
2. robin
3. ostrich
4. parrot
5. eagle
6. swan

Copymaster 14

1. **b)**
2. **a)**
3. **b)**

4. a)
5. a)
6. a)

Copymaster 15

1. Archie the small dinosaur woke up.
2. He saw that he was covered in little spikes.
3. Everyone laughed at him.
4. Archie ran into the forest.
5. The other dinosaurs began to search for him.
6. They came to the forest where the big Rexes lived.

Copymaster 16

1. Betsy and Bop
2. black
3. hutch
4. carrots lettuce
5. stroke

6–8. Check that the pictures match the text.

Copymaster 17

1. Adam was 7.
2. Dad didn't want to get up so early.
3. Nan and Grandad sent Adam a new football kit.
4. Dad was holding a cardboard box.
5. A scuffling sound was coming from the box.
6. A puppy was in the box.
7. Adam cuddled the puppy.
8. Adam called the puppy Sam.

Copymaster 18

2, 3, 6 are true and should be copied into the book.

7. They have had the hamsters for 6 weeks.
8. Chris calls his hamster Flip because it is very acrobatic.
9. They made an adventure playground.
10. They like apple and biscuit.

Copymaster 19

1. The letter was to Nan and Grandad.
2. Nicola wrote the letter.
3. Gran and Grandad sent Nicola a jigsaw and jeans.
4. They couldn't visit Nicola because Grandad had a bad leg.
5. Nicola's birthday was on Thursday 7th October.
6. Nicola was 8.
7. She took Amy, Holly, Angela and Katy.
8. They went ice skating and to McDonalds.
9. They had burgers and banana milkshake.

Copymaster 20

1. Jason is having a birthday party.
2. The party will be held at McDonalds.
3. The other treat will be swimming.
4. Samara will need to take her swimming costume and towel.
5. The party will be held on Saturday 4th May.
6. Samara must be at Jason's house (12 Lakeside Road, Newford).
7. Samara will spend 4 hours with Jason.
8. Jason will be 8 years old.

Copymaster 21

1. Seas-breeze waves-graves mile-isle bark-dark
2. Sam was a very good sailor.
   A dreadful storm blew up.
   The ship was tossed about and some sailors were drowned.
   Sam was shipwrecked on an island.
   Sam lit a fire outside his new home.
   Sam has sent a message in a bottle in the hope that he'll be rescued.

Copymaster 22

1. a)
2. b)
3. b)
4. a)
5. b)

Copymaster 23

Things you will need: seeds, 9cm pots, compost

1. Fill each pot with compost.
2. Push each seed 2cm down and cover it with compost.
3. Water the seed.
4. Put the pot in a warm, light place.
5. Water it when necessary.
6. Plant the sunflower at the back of a flowerbed.
7. Label it with your name.

Copymaster 24

1, 4, 6, 7, 9, 10 are true and should be copied into the book.

Copymaster 25

	Naresh	Daniel	Holly	Saria
Cheese and tomato pizza	✓	✗	✓	✗
Roast meat	✗	✓	✗	✓
Burger and chips	✗	✓	✗	✓
Ice cream	✗	✓	✓	✓
Fruit	✓	✗	✓	✓
Yogurt	✓	✓	✓	✓

1. Holly is a vegetarian.
2. Daniel and Saria like meat.
3. They all like yogurt.
4. Naresh and Holly like cheese.
5. Two children like vegetables.
6. Daniel and Saria would enjoy burgers, chips and ice cream.
7. Daniel doesn't eat vegetables or fruit.

Copymaster 26

1. She lived in a web in a high, dark corner of the shed.
2. Her web was silken.
3. He didn't mind her.
4. He didn't want Susie to go into his house.
5. A spider has 8 legs.
6. Susie ate flies.

7. Her sticky web caught flies for her.
8. Spiderlings galore appeared from her nest.
9. So Susie grew and grew!
10. Her hairy legs and the way she scuttled made Susie scary.

Copymaster 27

1. Romulus Remus
2. princes
3. uncle
4. basket
5. die
6. rescued
7. fed cared
8. shepherd
9. wife
10. city
11. king
12. Remus

Copymaster 28

1. **b)**
2. **a)**
3. **a)**
4. **b)**
5. **b)**
6. **a)**
7. **b)**
8. **b)**

Copymaster 29

1. birth/arrival
2. cot/crib
3. day
4. order
5. counted/registered
6. worried
7. long/hard
8. good
9. go/obey
10. donkey
11. stay/rest/sleep
12. baby
13. sleep/rest
14. star
15. stable
16. gifts/presents

Copymaster 30

1. **a)**
2. **a)**
3. **b)**
4. **b)**
5. **a)**
6. **b)**
7. **a)**
8. **b)**

Copymaster 31

1. Mrs. Jolly was a school caretaker.
2. She was friendly, nice and cuddly.
3. She had a cat.
4. She became a witch at the end of school each day.
5. She used her magic powers.
6. Her magic words were "Rise and shine!"
7. She had to clean the whole school and sweep the playground.
8. No, she was a good witch.
9. She sat and had a cup of tea.
10. The curtains drew themselves and the lights switched themselves off.
11. She swept the playground.
12. She swept the playground herself in case people saw a broom sweeping all by itself.

Copymaster 32

1. They were going because their father was ill and their mother was too busy looking after him.
2. He lived on a farm up on the moors.
3. They went in Granpa's pick-up truck.
4. He wouldn't move because towns felt like prison/he liked to see moors and sky all around him/he wanted to stay with his animals.
5. No – Mrs. Hammond came.
6. He packed jeans, shirts, sweaters, socks and a toy kangaroo.
7. She particularly wanted to stay there because she'd never seen the farm in winter.
8. Booker was a stuffed toy kangaroo; he was old and battered with one ear.
9. Scooter's real name was James.
10. He was called Scooter because he ran about so quickly.

Copymaster 33

1. She was looking forward to lunch-time because she had a special yogurt.
2. She had to finish her work.
3. She had brought an apple.
4. They were kept on a shelf.
5. She searched the other lunchboxes.
6. She was shocked because Emily was her best friend.
7. She decided to take the yogurt from Emily's box and put it in her own.
8. She was pleased because she wanted to punish her for stealing.
9. Mum thought Sally would be hungry because she had left her yogurt at home.
10. guilty/embarrassed/dreadful/awful/worried/frightened/mean

Copymaster 34

1, 3, 5, 7, 8, 9, 10, 12 are true and should be copied into the book.

Copymaster 35

1. He belongs to Mary's brother.
2. Mary is looking after Mickey because Chris is away.
3. Mary closes her eyes and hopes she is wrong because she can't find Mickey.
4. Mary did not shut the cage door properly.
5. She expects to see a twitching pink nose.
6. She looks under the shavings, in the jam jar and in the bedding.

7. She is dreading having to tell Chris that Mickey is lost.
8. Mum tells Mary to wash her hands because Mary has been cleaning the cage.
9. She doesn't tell Mum because she is hoping to find Mickey before Mum finds out he is gone.
10. She keeps going back to the shed to see if she can find Mickey.
11. She keeps looking at the ground because she expects to see Mickey at any moment.
12. She goes to the pet shop to buy a new mouse.

Copymaster 36

1. Emily was on the floor because she had been thrown/catapulted there from a web.
2. She heard a roaring noise.
3. She knew what it was because her mother had warned her about hoovers.
4. She couldn't escape because she was dazed and helpless.
5. A happy ending was the last thing Emily expected.
6. She felt two sharp pains.
7. She couldn't see or shout for help because she was in thick, choking black dust and dirt.
8. When the hoover was switched off, Emily struggled to the top of the pile of dust in the bag.
9. She met some woodlice.
10. They looked at Emily in a friendly manner.

Copymaster 37

1. Charlotte went to the zoo on her birthday.
2. Dad gave Charlotte a book about animals so that she could find out why Bamboo is a good name for a panda.
3. A panda's eyes, ears, arms and legs are black.
4. The panda comes from China.
5. In China it is cold and wet for many months of the year.
6. The panda's main food is bamboo.
7. The panda spends its day eating and sleeping.
8. The panda's sharp claws help it to climb trees.
9. There are few baby pandas because pandas like to live alone.
10. There are so few pandas left because large areas of bamboo forests have been cleared, so the panda has a smaller area in which to live and feed.

Copymaster 38

No snorkels
Think of others
Don't go out of your depth
Never run on the poolside
Swimming hats must be worn
Don't shout or scream
Don't pull anyone underwater
No food or drink permitted at the poolside
No smoking

Copymaster 39

1. You would avoid the Great Grizzly Bear, Gerry the Giraffe, Wally the Whale and the Monkey Playground.
2. It would cost £16 (or £15 with a family ticket).
3. It will cost £10.
4. It will cost £29 (or £25 with a family ticket).
5. The Monkey Playground will help them use up some of their energy.
6. She would like Gerry the Giraffe.
7. They would take them to Petra the Panda's Pizza Place.
8. They would go to Caroline the Camel's Cosy Café.
9. It is closed on Christmas Day.
10. It closes at 6p.m.
11. Eliza the Elephant would take you on a tour around the theme park.
12. You can go go-karting at Snakes Alive.
13. You might get very wet on Wally the Whale.
14. You would go on the Black Bat Ride.

Copymaster 40

1. They were going to help Gran and Grandad to sort out their rubbish.
2. It was half-term and Mum and Dad were at work.
3. Gran wanted to clear out all the rubbish so she could do some spring-cleaning.
4. b)
5. Daniel put the bottles in a box in case they got broken.
6. The glass is ground up, melted and put into moulds.
7. They felt very tired.
8. He wanted to take all the rubbish to the recycling bins and have lunch in the supermarket café.
9. He was going to help them to mend and paint the things.
10.

Paper	**Glass**
kitchen roll tubes	wine bottles
newspapers	jam jars
old drawing paper	a sauce bottle
old magazines	a pickle jar
old letters	

Metal	**Compost heap**
a bent paperclip	potato peelings
rusty nails	leftovers from lunch
a cola can	tea-bags
lager cans	an apple core
a soup tin	banana skins

Copymaster 41

1. Seymour was looking for a perfect place.
2. He had enough room and the desert needed rain.
3. **a)** He was not good at walking in sand.
   b) There was no shade and there were no caves.
   c) Sand got between his toes and scales.
   d) The desert was not much fun.
4. He blew them around and destroyed their homes.
5. No, the animals did not become his friends.
6. It mixed everything up.
7. They pointed the way across the sand.

Copymaster 42

The correct order is **c) f) i) a) e) b) g) d) j) h)**

Copymaster 43

1. Lou was looking after Simon because his Mum was at work.

2. Lou was working as a cleaner.
3. Simon saw pictures, a vase of tulips, a table and a telephone.
4. Lou had told Simon that the house was haunted.
5. It was a fat, stripey ginger cat.
6. There were velvet armchairs and sofas, a mirror and a mantelpiece.
7. The cat had been sleeping.
8. He sat down and squeaked when he spoke.
9. There was no sign that it was a haunted house.
10. There are few people worth making the effort to speak to.

Copymaster 44

1. The advert wanted you to buy new Zappers.
2. Zappers come in orange, lemon, lime and strawberry flavours.
3. Delicious/fruity/sugar-coated/crispy/crunchy/munchy

Copymaster 45

1. Italy → Denmark
2. holiday → raids
3. wood → treasure
4. flat → mountainous
5. France → Britain
6. south → north
7. Henry → Alfred
8. London → Danelaw
9. ferries → longboats
10. engines → sails
11. guns → bows and arrows
12. leather → metal

Copymaster 46

1. The Vikings came from Norway, Sweden and Denmark.
2. Odin was the most important god.
3. Thor was Odin's son.
4. Thor's most precious possession was his great hammer.
5. Asgard was the home of the gods.
6. Loki went to find the hammer.
7. He was disguised as a falcon.
8. Thrym, King of the Giants, had stolen the hammer and hidden it deep in the earth.
9. Thrym wouldn't return the hammer until Freyja became his wife.
10. Freyja had a fit of temper; she made the walls shake, rattled the furniture and broke her necklace.
11. Thor was disguised as Freyja.
12. He was wearing a bridal dress, a veil and jewellery.
13. She hadn't eaten or slept much because she was so excited about marrying Thrym.
14. He kept the promise that he would return the hammer.
15. Thor hoped to teach the lesson that no one could trick or beat the gods.

Copymaster 47

1. wrapped in the leaves of autumn
2. The flame is lit to show the way in the dark.
3. It means "let them be joined".
4. Ravana was the Demon King.
5. She had been taken to the island of Lanka.
6. He fought a dreadful battle.
7. It means "light the flame".
8. The moon and the stars are mentioned.
9. The poem is about Diwali.
10. Ravana had kidnapped Princess Sita, to marry her and rule the whole world.
11. Hanuman, King of the Monkeys, found Sita.
12. They are lit to welcome Rama home.

Copymaster 48

1. true
2. I can't tell
3. false
4. false
5. true
6. true
7. true
8. false
9. talented
10. competition
11. enraged
12. finally

Copymaster 49

1. He was small and green with webbed feet and eyes on stumpy antennae.
2. He wanted to borrow a spanner.
3. He had died.
4. Growing vegetables, keeping chickens and knitting kept Gran busy.
5. They had had trouble with the gears on the spacecraft.
6. The mechanic had left his tools back at base.
7. He was a steward.
8. He had a long way to go.
9. The spacecraft had gone without him.
10. isolated → alone
    unflappable → calm
    occasional → from time to time
    agitated → disturbed
    distinctly → clearly
    emergency → a sudden difficulty
    constructed → made

Copymaster 50

1. They lived in Athens.
2. Rich people had slaves.
3. Saffo had lessons in reading, writing, music and arithmetic.
4. Slaves and women were not allowed to vote.
5. "Democracy" means "government by the people"/"an elected government".
6. The men on the Pnyx governed Athens.
7. Hero spent more time at school because his family were rich.

Copymaster 51

1. Wales
2. monasteries
3. robbers'

4. walls smashed
5. harder
6. leave
7. sick
8. lessons
9. God
10. (drawing of a daffodil)

Copymaster 52

1. He was his brother.
2. They gave up being fishermen to follow Jesus.
3. The Romans were trying to stamp out Christianity.
4. Andrew was put to death on a cross.
5. The cross was shaped like an X.
6. A monk looked after Andrew's grave.
7. His body was taken to Scotland.
8. People celebrate St. Andrew's Day on November 30th.
9. (drawing of the Scottish flag)

Copymaster 53

Answers for ACROSS

6. BRAVE
7. GEORGE
8. JESUS
11. TERRIBLE
13. DRAGON
16. PRISON
17. RED ROSE
18. CITY
19. SOLDIER

Answers for DOWN

1. KILLED
2. SHEEP
3. CHRISTIAN
4. LAKE
5. LOCKED
9. SHARP
10. PRINCESS
12. ENGLAND
14. FIERY
15. APRIL

Copymaster 54

1. St. Patrick was born in Wales.
2. Patrick was sixteen when he was captured by the robbers.
3. He worked as a shepherd.
4. He missed his home and family.
5. They believed in many gods and magic.
6. He fled to France.
7. He was sixty when he returned to Ireland.
8. His first convert was the King of Ireland.
9. He spent the rest of his life building churches and converting people to Christianity.
10. The national plant of Ireland is the shamrock.
11. We celebrate St. Patrick's Day on 17th March.
12. influenced/inspired
    changing/transforming
    in the end
    clever/competent

Copymaster 55

2, 4, 5, 8, 10 are true and should be copied into the book.

Copymaster 56

Answers for ACROSS

1. STONE
2. WHIPPED
5. BOARDING
7. MOUNTAINS
11. HARD
13. SHIELD
14. EASY
15. PERFECT
16. SPARTA

Answers for DOWN

1. SEVEN
3. EXERCISE
4. SWORD
6. STEAL
8. SOLDIERS
9. STRICT
10. HOME
12. ARMY
13. SPEAR

Copymaster 57

1. They were taking the Martian to the village fête.
2. They wrapped him up so no one could really see him.
3. He admired the garage, the bright signs and the flags.
4. No, Gran did not agree with him.
5. He saw baked beans and a cornflake display.
6. Peter did not admire the display because he was used to it.
7. installed
8. swathed
9. drape
10. dimly
11. visible
12. nosy
13. gazed
14. fascinated
15. accepted
16. declared
17. anxiously
18. garish
19. doubtfully
20. angle

Copymaster 58

1. Ben was unhappy because he didn't want to go to a new school.
2. She had told her about a big, rough boy.
3. She didn't want to worry him.
4. He wanted a pet, especially a cat.
5. Santi's owner was called Mrs. Shastri.
6. Dad called the cat Santi Claws.
7. He gave it that nickname because it dug its claws in you.
8. They lived near a busy road and there was no one to look after it.
9. You have to feed it, groom it and give it somewhere to sleep.

Copymaster 59

1. They are robotic dinosaurs.
2. Max's Dad made them.
3. They were robbers.
4. She got her name from busting into houses.
5. He got his name from stuffing stolen things into binbags.
6. Binbag's idea was to use the dinosaurs on a robbery.
7. They would be able to steal jewellery.
8. They stole Triceratops.
9. He pushed a button and grabbed the levers.
10. They travelled fast.
11.

Binbag	**Buster**
dishonest	dishonest
sneaky	strong
thin	enthusiastic

scrawny
quick
enthusiastic
cunning
athletic
tattooed
well-built
powerful

Copymaster 60

1. The Great Wall has been standing for more than 2,000 years.
2. It was built to keep out China's enemies.
3. It is in the north.
4. The Emperor ordered it to be built.
5. Thousands of men built it.
6. Many men died.
7. He was a good builder.
8. The men were tired and they were thin, and they were beaten by the soldiers.
9. Meng cried because her husband was dead.
10. The Emperor would build her husband a fine tomb if she married him.
11. She hated the Emperor because he had taken her husband away.
12. She threw herself in the river and became a silver fish.

Copymaster 61

1. The story takes place in Egypt.
2. They brought the news that the Queen Cat had died.
3. She lived in the Temple of Bastet.
4. They would recognise the Queen Cat when they saw her.
5. She would not have any particular features.
6. Mew-Sheri decided to try to find her.
7. Her two sisters were called Zaita and Tiya.
8. No, they didn't think she would find the Queen Cat.
9. She would have to search in the Delta and Nubia.
10. holy/special
11. contemptuous/jeering/sarcastic
12. place where a river mouth breaks into several streams

Copymaster 62

1. Musah was hot/thirsty/exhausted.
2. He thought he was lucky because he had a job.
3. They were searching for an ancient tomb.
4. Howard Carter was in charge of the expedition.
5. Lord Carnarvon was paying for the search.
6. They are called archaeologists.
7. They are called labourers.
8. He was losing hope because the tomb had not been found.
9. He stubbed his foot on it.
10. It was one of the steps leading down to the tomb.
11. His find led to the tomb of Tutankhamun.
12. leave
13. banged against
14. went near to
15. without being touched

Copymaster 63

1. They hid because they were afraid of the dragon.
2. He rode a motorbike.
3. He thought Sir Garibald would be killed.
4. He stammered.
5. He frightened people by stamping and breathing fire.
6. He felt misunderstood/sad/cross.
7. He was trying to keep warm.
8. He said that he was vegetarian.
9. He felt sorry for the dragon.
10. He gave him his scarf, gloves and socks.
11. He needed them because it was cold on his motorbike.
12. The story has a happy ending because no one was hurt/everyone was happy/the dragon went home.

Copymaster 64

1. The figures were made from straw.
2. The execution was on January 31st, 1606.
3. He shivered because it was cold and windy and his clothes were thin.
4. Thomas Winter's brother was called Robert.
5. He had already been executed.
6. They had tried to destroy the House of Lords.
7. Eight men had been sentenced to death.
8. He had been tortured and couldn't climb the ladder.
9. "I ask the King and God for forgiveness. I am not afraid to die."
10. We light bonfires and fireworks and burn a guy on the bonfire.

Copymaster 65

1. two left feet → a habit of doing the wrong thing
   has a point → is right
   the truth of the matter is → the fact is
   faster than smoke → very quickly
   got under my uncle's skin → annoyed my uncle
   got his hands dirty → did some real work
   tapped the side of his nose → told her to mind her own business
   empty-handed → with nothing
2. There were nine people in the family.
3. He was very pleased with himself.
4. Uncle brought Father a present because he wanted to show Father that he could achieve something.
5. Father tripped over it and broke his toe.
6. He lost some weapons.
7. He threatened to put him in the pot.

Copymaster 66

1. Ernest hadn't seen the stranger before because he was new to the village.
2. The stranger was an English Setter.
3. He said that Ernest was a Gloucestershire Cow Dog.
4. The stranger couldn't see Ernest's expression because he had hair over his face.
5. Ernest felt astonishment, then excitement, then satisfaction.

6. He thought they didn't know what breed he was because they were foreigners.
7. decent → respectable
   considered → thought
   prevented → stopped
   expression → look
   satisfaction → pleasure
   recognised → known

Copymaster 67

2, 4, 6, 7 are true and should be copied into the book.

9. The population increased and many machines were invented.
10. Children worked in factories/down mines/on farms/as street traders.
11. They wanted children to work because they could pay them low wages.
12. They sent their children out to work because they needed the money.

Copymaster 68

1. Chris bought a Super-Ray Mark III remote-controlled car.
2. He is writing the letter because the car won't work.
3. He is writing to the manager of Bardale Toys.
4. Dad is so cross because they made a special journey to buy the car.
5. He saved his money.
6. He had looked forward to getting it for a long time.
7. They went to buy the car on Saturday 27th May.
8. He wants the manager to replace the car or give him a refund.
9. He tried it with different batteries.

Copymaster 69

1. He was running away from his Roman master/the sentry.
2. He was being chased because he had escaped from the camp.
3. He was going to be fed to the lions.
4. Androcles was too terrified to move.
5. The lion did not attack him because he remembered that Androcles had helped him.
6. A thorn was in it.
7. They were taken to the arena.
   hornt → thorn
   scrndAelo → Androcles
   easerrtd → arrested
   refomed → freedom
   inlo → lion
   nreaa → arena

Copymaster 70

1. Danny has a key because his Mum isn't at home and he has to let himself into his house.
2. The key is on a piece of string round his neck so he doesn't lose it.
3. She thinks it's a shame that he's left at home alone.
4. He watches TV, eats crisps and goes to see his friend.
5. It means "rather deaf", "unable to hear well".
6. She leaves him because she's always rushing off somewhere.
7. She uses a taxi.
8. He scoops up the kiss because it means a lot to him.
9. She repeats this because she is sad that a child of seven should be left alone.
10. beg

Copymaster 71

1. The story comes from the Koran.
2. It is the Muslim holy book.
3. The story shows that Allah is merciful and kind.
4. She told them to stay close to their nests, gather food and not panic.
5. A terrible noise was causing the ants concern.
6. She went to the top of the tallest nest.
7. The huge grey shape was Sulaiman's army.
8. The army's marching feet were causing the noise.
9. Allah had taught him the language of the animals.
10. He told them to stop marching.
11. They trod very carefully.
12. merciful → kind, forgiving
    summoned → called together
    peered → looked carefully
    valley → low area between hills
    magnificent → splendid
    avoid → keep away from
    prophet → inspired teacher/one who reveals things about the future
    mighty → powerful
    instructed → ordered

Copymaster 72

1. The hurricane is called Gilbert.
2. They ran away.
3. They were made of zinc.
4. She describes each gust of wind as a sneeze.
5. He cleaned his nails and sprinkled sand everywhere.
6. He destroyed our food and crops.
7. He disconnected them.
8. She repeats the lines to emphasise how much the people fear a hurricane.

Copymaster 73

1. He was going on holiday.
2. His ship was captured by pirates.
3. They decided to ransom him.
4. He was shocked at how little the pirates asked.
5. He had to wait below deck.
6. They demanded fifty talents of gold.
7. Caesar was released.
8. They laughed because he was young/he'd have difficulty in catching them.
9. He caught and killed the pirates.
10. Caesar's revenge
11. ask → demand
    captured → taken
    fame → greatness
    ruler → dictator
    knew → recognised
    bargain → deal

Copymaster 74

1, 3, 4, 6, 7, 9, 10, 11 are true and should be copied into the book.

Copymaster 75

1. They were shocked because the impossible had happened, and the *Mary Rose* had sunk.
2. King Henry VIII was watching the fleet.
3. This event took place in the year 1545.
4. The English fleet was setting sail to fight the French fleet.
5. The *Mary Rose* carried 207 guns and 500 men.
6. The ship was overloaded and the weight was not evenly balanced, so water passed in and made the ship tip over.
7. He was horrified.
8. The *Mary Rose* lay on the seabed for 437 years.
9. They found tools and everyday items, and skeletons.
10. The *Mary Rose* is now in a museum in Portsmouth.

Copymaster 76

1. The correct order is **f) d) b) g) a) e) c)**
2. They were brothers.
3. They escaped by cart and chariot.
4. They found safety in Cumae.
5. They intended to make a new life in Rome.

Copymaster 77

1. It was evening.
2. They lived on the banks of the Nile.
3. The children were called Hapti and Lostris.
4. He was a scribe.
5. They had a cat and some kittens.
6. They ate goose, vegetables and fruit.
7. Tati's family put the Book of the Dead in her tomb.
8. Her heart had to be weighed.
9. Anubis weighed Tati's heart.
10. Thoth was the god of wisdom.
11. The Gobbler was disappointed with the results of the test.
12. They smiled to welcome her to the Blessed Fields.
13. The Blessed Fields were the afterlife – a lovely place of sunshine, food, plants and flowers where no one was ever ill or poor.
14. Our name for the Blessed Fields would be "Heaven".
15. It taught them to be honest and kind.

Copymaster 78

1. King Philip of Spain was intending to invade England.
2. His wife had been Queen of England.
3. The Armada was making for Calais.
4. They were going to Calais to pick up their soldiers.
5. Beacon fires were the signal.
6. The English fleet sailed from Plymouth.
7. The English fleet met the Armada near the Isle of Wight.
8. The Spanish fleet was scattered by blazing ships sent in by the English.
9. Other Spanish ships were destroyed by storms and by the English.
10. The brave seamen were Admiral Lord Howard, Sir Francis Drake and John Hawkins.

Copymaster 79

1. The Buddha was born in a small village on the borders of India and Nepal.
2. His mother was Queen Maya.
3. His real name was Siddhartha Gautama.
4. "Buddha" means "the Enlightened One".
5. Buddhists follow eight rules.
6. The Buddha's tooth is kept in the city of Kandy.
7. Kandy is a beautiful city/is on the edge of a lake/is in Sri Lanka/has a great temple on a small hill.
8. The festival is held once a year, in August, on the night of the full moon.
9. The tooth is taken round the city in a casket on an elephant's back.
10. The elephants are painted/wear bright cloths/wear brilliant gold head-dresses with silver studs and coloured glass "jewels".
11. There is dancing, fire swallowing and fireworks.

Copymaster 80

1. clanging
2. mournful
3. hushed
4. shuffling
5. peak
6. anxiously
7. signs
8. cured
9. escape
10. The dead were collected after midnight so people didn't see all the bodies.
11. She had seen a large red cross on the door of Benjamin's house.
12. The first symptoms of the plague were shivering, fever and a cough.
13. The poor people didn't leave because they had nowhere to go.
14. **a), c), d), f)** should be written down.

Copymaster 81

1. They were looking forward to Passover/Pesach.
2. The Jewish people were slaves in Egypt.
3. God told Moses to persuade the Pharaoh to let the Israelites go.
4. God promised them a land of their own.
5. God sent the plagues to force the Pharaoh to let the Israelites go.
6. The final plague was the Angel of Death killing the first-born son in every house.
7. They escaped by painting crosses in lamb's blood on their doors.
8. He let them go, and then chased them.
9. It opened for them.
10. The Passover meal is called Seder.
11. Lamb stands for the blood used to paint crosses on the doors.
    Bitter herbs stand for slavery.
    An egg stands for new life.
    Green vegetables stand for spring.
    Charoset stands for the sweetness of freedom.
    Salt water stands for tears.

Copymaster 82

1. Lilly knew that Drina wasn't a servant from the way she spoke.
2. Lilly wasn't allowed to talk to Drina because she was only a servant.
3. Drina's best friend was a doll.
4. The governess had put holly under Drina's chin to make her hold her head up.
5. They tried to keep quiet in case the Butler heard.
6. She was too busy to meet Drina after tea.
7. Lilly felt sorry for Drina because she was lonely.
8. inquisitive → curious
   command → order
   governess → teacher
   exhaustion → tiredness

Copymaster 83

1. There were four children.
2. He was not to touch the sharp tools.
3. He cut his eye with a knife.
4. adored → loved
   infection → a spreading disease
   method → way
   system → scheme
   scrap → waste
   outstanding → very good
   cope → manage
   tragic → sad

Copymaster 84

1. He pulled the sword Excalibur from a stone.
2. He became vain and proud.
3. She was sewing/working on some embroidery.
4. The Lady of the Lake appeared in the room.
5. If Arthur forgot that the magic sword brought him his power, his nephew Mordred would kill him.
6. She was very anxious about Arthur and watched him carefully.
7. Arthur was Mordred's uncle.
8. arrogant boastful thoughtless proud vain
9. anxious patient careful loving faithful
10. They thought that no one could harm him; he was like a god.

Copymaster 85

1. The correct order is: **c), d), e), a), f), b)**
   belongings → possessions
   disaster → tragedy
   blaze → fire
   lucky → fortunate
   warm → mild
   troubles → plight

Copymaster 86

Answers for ACROSS

3. ADOLF HITLER
6. KITTY
8. JEWISH
9. AUGUST
10. AMSTERDAM
14. STARVATION
15. FLOOR
16. MR. FRANK
17. SILENT

Answers for DOWN

1. EIGHT
2. GERMANY
4. OFFICE BLOCK
5. JUNE
7. TYPHUS
11. ANNE FRANK
12. TRAIN
13. HOLLAND

Copymaster 87

1. Julius Caesar wanted to invade Britain because of the fertile land, food, slaves and minerals.
2. He didn't try to invade because he needed a bigger army.
3. He invaded, with limited success.
4. Emperor Claudius invaded more than 90 years later.
5. The Romans made new roads, houses, bridges and forts.
6. Queen Boudicca led a rebellion against the Romans.
7. Hadrian ordered a wall to be built to keep out fierce northern tribes.
8. The Roman armies had to go and fight in Europe.
9. **Answers for ACROSS**
   1. SCOTLAND
   9. BEFORE CHRIST
   11. LEGION
   12. CARACTACUS
   13. ICENI
   14. POISONED

   Answers for DOWN
   2. CLAUDIUS
   3. JULIUS CAESAR
   4. ROME
   5. HADRIAN
   6. FORTS
   7. COLCHESTER
   8. SLAVES
   9. BOUDICCA
   10. ROADS

Copymaster 88

1. Halim brought the message.
2. The message meant that the embalming of Tutankhamun's body was finished.
3. Menset prepared bodies for burial by mummifying them.
4. It took about 70 days.
5. The body had to be washed in palm oil/emptied of internal organs/filled with linen pads/perfumed/stitched up/covered in natron/bandaged.
6. Tutankhamun had died.
7. They placed golden masks and jewellery on the body.
8. The tomb was in the Valley of the Kings in Thebes.
9. The coffin was taken by sledge and barge.
10. Everything needed for the afterlife was sealed in the tomb.
11. **Answers for ACROSS**
    5. STONE JARS
    7. EIGHTEEN
    8. ANUBIS
    9. PHARAOH
    10. KNELT
    11. BURIAL CHAMBER
    13. NATRON
    14. MENSET
    16. HALIM
    17. THEBES
    18. RESIN

    Answers for DOWN
    1. LINEN
    2. FUNERAL BARGE
    3. OXEN
    4. SARCOPHAGUS
    6. TUTANKHAMUN
    9. PALM
    12. EMBALMER
    15. NILE

Copymaster 89

1. Guru Nanak was adventurous, kind, honest and wise.
2. Guru Nanak is famous because he was the founder of the Sikh religion.
3. Mardana was his companion.
4. People travelled to Multan to seek advice from priests and holy men.
5. The priests thought it would be bad for their business.
6. There are enough holy men here already and we don't want you.
7. He carried the bowl carefully so as not to spill the milk.
8. He wanted to drink it.
9. He put a jasmine flower in it.
10. Guru Nanak's message was that just as the fragile flower did not cause the milk to spill, so he would not cause trouble in the city.
11. companion → friend
    tiring → exhausting
    manner → kinds
    seek → ask
    tempting → appealing
    stooped → bent
    fragile → delicate

Copymaster 90

1. fit
2. body of a ship
3. unit of measurement for the speed of a ship
4. leave
5. those who were not killed
6. The Titanic was sailing to New York.
7. It means "first voyage".
8. The hull was divided into sixteen compartments.
9. Coal was used to fuel the engines.
10. It was huge and luxurious.
11. Six compartments were said to be damaged by the ice.
12. It means "Save Our Souls" (help needed).
13. The *Carpathia* picked up the message.
14. The call was never received.
15. There were not enough lifeboats.

Copymaster 91

1. running → fleeing
2. ambition → aim
3. tired → exhausted
4. warning → alerting
5. killed → annihilated
6. saw → witnessed
7. broken → punctuated
8. faint → muffled
9. plaguing → harassing
10. noise → cacophony
11. They were pursuing 1,000 Japanese soldiers.
12. They were going to mainland Burma.
13. They had to cross a swamp.
14. They didn't want to alert the British troops.
15. The crocodiles attacked during the night.
16. Bruce Wright wasn't hurt because he was in a barge.
17. Shots/screams/muffled sounds/a hellish cacophony were heard.
18. Nothing could be seen because it was dark.

Copymaster 92

1. mounting → growing
   occurred → happened
   locally → nearby
   converted → altered
   miraculous → amazing
   rubble → debris
   conscious → awake
   astonished → surprised
   state → announce
   silently → noiselessly
2. **Answers for ACROSS**
   1. WARDROBE
   3. ANGELA
   5. ROCKET
   8. RUBBLE
   9. CHANDLER
   10. TARGET
   11. DESTRUCTION
   16. EXPLOSIVE
   18. PILOT
   19. ACCURATE

   Answers for DOWN
   2. DOODLEBUG
   4. GARDEN
   6. FLATS
   7. SIREN
   10. TWICKENHAM
   12. TWELVE
   13. FIFTEEN
   14. PETER
   15. INJURED
   17. LONDON

Copymaster 93

1. She heard a strange noise.
2. She was going to school.
3. A V1 rocket bomb, or doodlebug, had caused the explosion.
4. She fell and was trapped under the wardrobe.
5. Angela felt frightened/terrified/amazed/shocked/trapped.
6. The rubble was moved by firemen, ambulancemen and air-raid wardens.
7. Her mother was the most seriously injured.
8. Their lives had been changed by the rationing of food and clothing.
9. They cut up and altered their own clothing/cut up tablecloths and sheets to make clothes.
10. "Rationing" means "a fixed and limited amount".
11. Angela missed sweets.
12.

Rationed	Not rationed
jam cheese butter meat bacon tea eggs sweets	vegetables

Copymaster 94

1. Jupiter is the biggest planet.
2. Jupiter, Saturn, Uranus and Neptune are bigger than Earth.
3. Saturn has seventeen moons.
4. Pluto is the coldest planet because it's furthest from the sun.
5. Some planets have shorter days than Earth because they turn at different speeds.
6. Pluto takes the longest time to go round the sun.
7. Pluto has the smallest diameter.
8. Mercury would be too hot for people to live on.
9. Earth and Pluto have only one moon.
10. Venus has the longest day.

Copymaster 95

1. Llewellyn House was built during the reign of Queen Victoria.
2. Llewellyn House is in Wales.
3. You could go by train and bus, or Greenline bus.
4. They had seven children.
5. There were six servants.
6. They slept in bedrooms in the attic.
7. He owned a coalmine.
8. It would cost £10.
9. Thomas, Robert and Bethan were cared for by the nurse.
10. "Portable" means "movable".
11. The water was heated in the kitchen and carried upstairs.
12. You could look in the dining room and in the kitchen.
13. You could visit the old coalmine and the miners' cottages.
14. A visit to Llewellyn House would be a good way to find out about the Victorians because it shows you exactly what life was like.

Copymaster 96

1. Megan didn't think she was lucky because she was homesick/had to get up early/had to work very hard.
2. Her working day was seventeen hours long.
3. She had been working there for three years.
4. She cleared grates/lit the fire/heated and carried up water/did the washing and drying up/prepared vegetables/helped with the laundry/scrubbed the kitchen.
5. She had mutton stew, bread and cheese and the occasional treat of ham and cakes.
6. Dilys wasn't sorry because he was a hard man.
7. She had two days off every month.
8. He was a coalface worker.
10. scullery → small kitchen used for washing dishes
11. kind → good-hearted
12. kept a tight hold on the pursestrings → kept control of the money
13. skilled → expert
14. regular → at equal intervals
15. mutton → sheep meat
16. routine → order of daily activities
17. chores → jobs
18. fever → illness which gives the sufferer a high temperature

Copymaster 97

1. Sophie is writing to thank Mrs. Frankum for arranging the visit.
2. She runs the Katesgrove Victorian Schoolroom.
3. She has collected slates, old books, pews, desks, clothes and other items.
4. Sophie thought it was fun to dress up.
5. They did arithmetic and handwriting.
6. Andrew was frightened because he had smudged his writing and thought he might get the cane.
7. His punishment was to wear a dunce's cap.
8. They had to be silent and still.
9. They thought the visit was very interesting, but they were glad to get back to their own school.
10. Sophie is in Class 6P.
11. It is in Reading.
12. It is in Thatcham, Berkshire.
13. **Answers for ACROSS**
    2. PLEASED
    4. DUNCE'S CAP
    5. CANE
    6. SLATES
    7. MRS. FRANKUM
    8. INTERESTING
    10. CORNER
    11. COPYBOOK
    12. PINAFORE
    13. SOPHIE
    14. CLASS 6P

    Answers for DOWN
    1. VICTORIAN SCHOOL
    3. ARITHMETIC
    4. DESKS
    9. NERVOUS

Copymaster 98

1. It was a village.
2. The children were gathering fruit and working in the fields.
3. The Wesleyan School treat was on July 21st.
4. They had been soaked by the rain.
5. The headmaster was absent to attend examinations in London.
6. August 2nd was a Bank Holiday and the school was closed.
7. "Running the streets" means "running wild".
8. Mr. Tuttle, a school manager, visited the school on 14th September.
9. They went to church because it was St. Matthew's Day.
10. An Attendance Officer made sure that the children went to school.

Copymaster 99

1. Winter was nearly over and spring was on its way.
2. the snow was melting
3. they rushed into Midgard
4. the travellers were caught in a late snowstorm
5. the heavy snowfall ended
6. the bright sunshine bursting through the thick clouds
7. the growing patches of pale blue sky
8. the flat green fields of Midgard
9. towards its source
10. Feeling happy and sleepy

Copymaster 100

1. Hotel Calypso would be better for families with children.
2. It is near the beach/offers safe bathing/has family rooms/has cots and highchairs/offers early teas/has a babysitting and crèche service/has a TV room/has a games arcade/has crazy golf/has go-karts/has an adventure playground/has a Crocodile Club/has a water park/has a weekly treasure hunt.
3. Both hotels have shower and WC in all rooms/ lifts/buffet breakfast/poolside bar/sunbeds/ barbecues/coach trips.
4. The Sol Restaurant in Hotel Lombard offers waiter service.

5. Hotel Lombard has more places to eat.
6. Hotel Lombard lies outside the town centre.
7. Sunbeds are free in Hotel Lombard but not in Hotel Calypso.
8. All the rooms have full air-conditioning/a bath/ a sea view/a balcony/tea- and coffee-making facilities.

Copymaster 101

1. powerless → unable
2. contingent → group
3. notorious → infamous
4. lurched → jumped
5. outskirts → borders
6. mingle → mix
7. wayward → difficult
8. apparently → clearly
9. occupied → busy
10. evade → escape
11. locations → places
12. eventually → finally
13. daring → bold
14. His heart lurched with fear.
15. The robbery had taken place on the London to Bath road on Hounslow Heath.
16. He had held up the coach in a small copse.
17. They were afraid of being shot.
18. They were going to Bath.
19. He had so few friends because he was a hunted man – a thief.
20. His skill as a horseman and his determination helped him to escape.
21. They admired his nerve in committing robberies and his skill in not getting caught.

Copymaster 102

1. shielded → shaded
   pilfering → stealing
   thrashed → wriggled
   spring → jump
   flee → escape
   dangling → hanging
   delicacy → treat
   devoured → ate
   surveyed → watched
   ceased → stopped
   direst → worst
2. Harry's plans were to steal and eat his fill.
3. The cat ate him.
4. She wanted to eat the rat in peace.
5. She jumped up on to a rain barrel and then on to a windowsill and walked along a beam on to the roof.
6. She could be seen because there was bright moonlight.
7. She was gorgeous, with ginger fur, delicate features, a sharp chin and a small pink nose.
8. She looked out over London.
9. Gruesome murders, dire tragedies, death and disaster could happen.
10. She saw a man with a lantern.
11. It was autumn.
12. She thought they were ugly, cruel and stupid.
13. She pretended to like them so that they would give her milk and scraps.
14. It was quiet/threatening/depressing.
15. Although it was quiet, trouble often happened at just such a time.

Name ____________________ Date ____________

Who is my Mum?

Finish these sentences.

Use the names and the pictures to find the words you need.

Only you can do the last one!!

1 This is my Mum. **hen**  I am a __________. 

2 This is my Mum. **sow**  I am a __________. 

3 This is my Mum. **frog**  I am a __________. 

4 This is my Mum. **cat**  I am a __________. 

5 This is my Mum. **sheep**  I am a __________. 

6 This is my Mum. **cow**  I am a __________. 

7 This is *my* Mum.  and this is *me!* 

kitten **chick** **tadpole** **piglet** **calf** **lamb**

Name ______________________ Date ____________

I like ...

Alina	Peter	Jake	Nicola
I like to draw.	I like ice cream.	I like to read.	I like to cook.
Amy	**Nadim**	**Tara**	**Ben**
I like to swim.	I like football.	I like to run.	I like to help.

Answer these questions in sentences.

Don't forget the CAPITAL letters and full stops.

The first one has been done for you.

1 Who likes to run? Tara likes to run.

2 Who likes ice cream? ______________________

3 Who likes to draw? ______________________

4 Who likes to read? ______________________

5 Who likes football? ______________________

6 Who likes to help? ______________________

7 Who likes to cook? ______________________

8 Who likes to swim? ______________________

9 What do *you* like? ______________________

____

Name ______________________ Date ______________

At the Seaside

The Jones family are at the seaside.

Look at the picture and see what they are doing.

Use the words in the picture to finish these sentences.

1 Sally and Kate are making a ______________.

2 Dad is eating an ______________.

3 Mum is reading a ______________.

4 Spot is playing with a ______________.

5 Sam is collecting water in his ______________.

6 There is a ______________ on the top of the cliff.

7 The ______________ is very hot.

Join these words to make things you would find on the beach.

Write the words on the lines.

The first one has been done for you.

8 sea	castle	seashell
9 sun	shell	______________
10 sand	house	______________
11 light	shine	______________

Name ______________________ Date ______________

The Playground

two
sunny
smiling
pram
woman
girl
seesaw
slide

Look at the picture and then read these sentences.
One word is wrong in each sentence.
Find the correct word from the list.
The first one has been done for you.

1 A man is pushing a ~~trolley~~. pram

2 A man is pushing the swing. ______________

3 A boy has fallen over. ______________

4 There are two children on the roundabout. ______________

5 Three children are at the ice cream van. ______________

6 It is a rainy day. ______________

7 A boy is climbing the tree. ______________

8 The baby is crying. ______________

Name ______________________ Date ____________

On the Farm

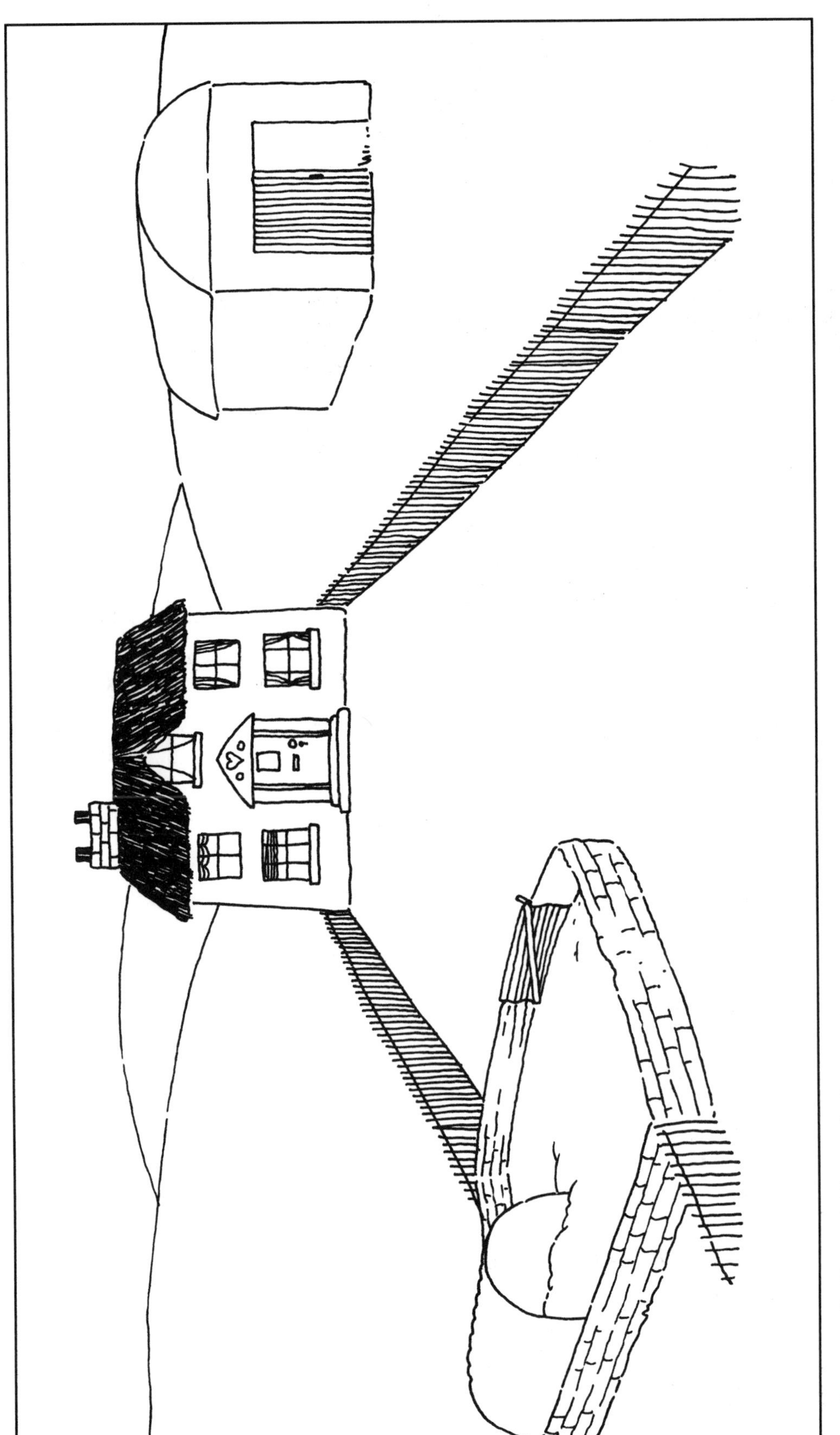

Look carefully at the picture.

Now draw:
- a tractor in one field
- two pigs in the sty
- three birds flying over the farmhouse
- three cows in the other field
- the farmer feeding some hens by the barn
- a scarecrow in a field

Colour the picture.

Name ______________________ Date ______________

In the Classroom

Look carefully at the picture.

Now draw:

- a picture of a pig on the blackboard
- two children at each table
- a clock on the wall
- three pencils on each table
- two books on each table
- the sun shining through the window
- a bin under one table

Colour the picture.

Name ______________________ Date ______________

Going to School

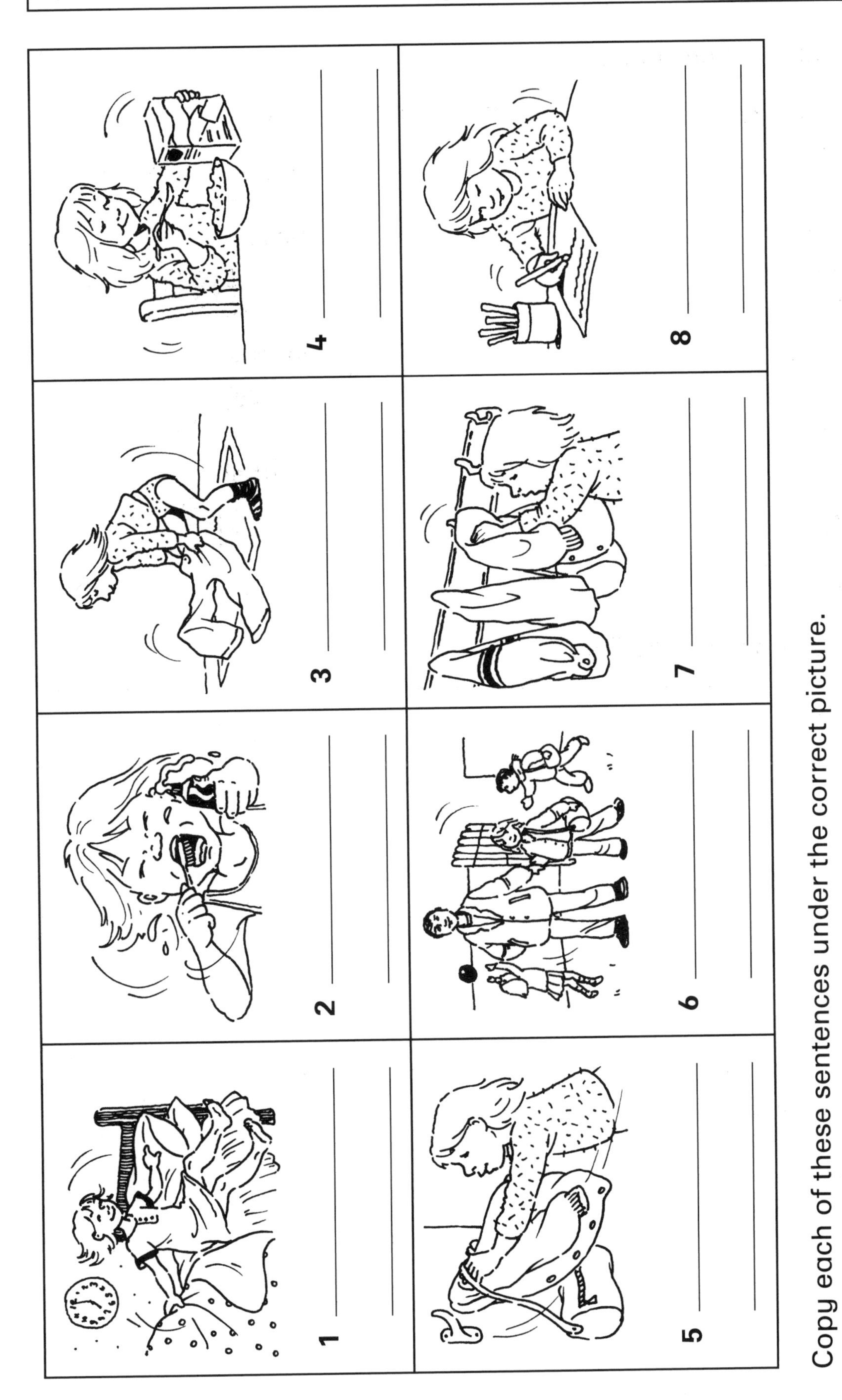

Copy each of these sentences under the correct picture.

I get ready for school.

I get dressed.

I hang my coat and bag in the cloakroom.

My Dad takes me to school.

I do my work.

I get up at seven o'clock.

I eat my breakfast.

I wash and brush my teeth.

Name ______________________ Date ______________

Where do I Live?

Join the animals to their homes.

1 A horse lives in a

2 A dog lives in a

3 A bird lives in a

4 A pig lives in a

but I live in a ____________.

sty

nest

stable

kennel

Draw a picture of where you live.

Now write your address.

____

____

____

Name ______________________ Date ______________

Words and Pictures

Draw a picture in each box to go with the sentences.

Mrs. Patel is taking Arun and Tara to school.
Arun is carrying his football and Tara is carrying her lunch box.

It is a sunny day.
Mr. Lee is helping May-Ling to feed her rabbit.

Sam has fallen off his new green bike.
Gran has put a plaster on his knee and is trying to mend his bike.

Mrs. Smith is wearing her blue jeans and a red shirt.
She is washing her new black car.

Name ____________________ Date ____________

Sam's Snowman

He ran out and made footprints in the snow. He was going to make a big snowman. ◯	He washed and dressed very quickly. ◯	Sam looked out of his bedroom window. It had snowed in the night. ◯
Sam put on his anorak, scarf, hat, gloves and boots. ◯	Sam made a lovely snowman. Mum put a hat and scarf on him. ◯	Mum made him have a hot drink and some toast for breakfast. ◯

Number the pictures, putting them in the correct order.
Now write the sentences down in the correct order.

1 ____________________
2 ____________________
3 ____________________
4 ____________________
5 ____________________
6 ____________________

Name ______________________ Date ______________

Travelling Around

Match the correct picture to each person and write the correct word in each space.

1 I carry heavy loads.
I drive a long way.
I deliver food to shops.
I drive a

_________________________.

2 I take lots of passengers.
I stop at stations.
I travel on rails.
I drive a

_________________________.

3 I wear a helmet and goggles.
I travel on two wheels.
I can travel very fast.
I ride a

_________________________.

4 I sometimes have to drive fast.
I have a siren.
I help sick people.
I drive an

_________________________.

bike

plane

lorry

motorbike

tractor

car

ambulance

train

5 I travel a very long way.
I go very fast.
I can go very high.
I pilot a

_________________________.

6 I drive my children to school.
I put shopping in the boot.
I buy petrol at the garage.
I drive a

_________________________.

7 I am a farmer.
I travel on big back wheels.
I can pull heavy loads.
I drive a

_________________________.

8 I wear a helmet.
I don't travel very fast.
I have a bell.
I ride a

_________________________.

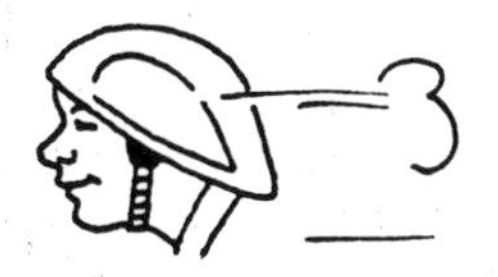

Name ______________________ Date ______________

My Town

Bookshop **Fish shop** **Shoe shop** **Post Office** **Toy shop** **Sweet shop** **Post Office van**

This is a picture of my town.
There are lots of different shops.

Look at the picture carefully and then write the answers to these questions in sentences.
Remember the CAPITAL letters and full stops.

1 Which shop would you like to go in?

I would like to go in the ______________________.

2 Where would you go to post a letter?

____

3 Where would you go to buy a book?

____

4 Where do you think the van is going?

The van is going to the ______________________.

5 Which shop is to the right of the fish shop?

____

6 What does the writing on the road say?

____

7 Write the numbers on these pictures so they are in the same order as the pictures at the top.

Shoe shop	Post Office	Sweet shop	Bookshop	Toy shop	Fish shop
____	____	____	____	____	____

Name ______________________________ Date ______________

What am I?

1 I am black and white. I have small wings but I cannot fly.
I am a very good swimmer. My home is very cold.

I am a ____________ .

2 I am small with a red chest. I hop around your garden.
I eat insects and worms. You might put bread out for me to eat.
My picture is often on Christmas cards.

I am a ____________ .

3 I am a huge bird. I am taller than a man. I cannot fly but I have long legs and a long neck and I can run very fast. I live in Africa.

I am an ____________ .

4 I am a noisy bird. I squawk but I can learn to talk. My feathers are very colourful and bright. I come from hot, tropical forests.

I am a ____________ .

5 I am a large, golden-brown bird. I have big, powerful wings.
My beak is sharp and curved. My claws are strong to grip my prey.

I am an ____________ .

6 I am white with a long, slender neck. I have webbed feet.
I can swim gracefully through water, walk on land and fly.

I am a ____________ .

Name ______________________ Date ____________

Mrs. Smith's Crocodile

Mrs. Smith had a pet budgie but she wanted something more exciting, so she went to the pet shop and bought a baby crocodile. But baby animals have a habit of growing very quickly. Mrs. Smith had to make a large pond in the garden. Crocodiles also have some rather nasty habits!

One day when Sweetypie was lazing in the pond, the cat next door came into the garden. Sweetypie watched the cat, then he opened his mouth as the cat went by and swallowed it whole.

"Mrs. Smith!" cried the woman next door. "Your crocodile has just eaten my cat!"

"Nonsense," said Mrs. Smith. "I expect your cat has gone indoors. Sweetypie wouldn't hurt a fly."

And Sweetypie smiled. He had a very large smile, exposing 100 shiny white teeth. "Miaow," he said.

From *Mrs. Smith's Crocodile* by Linda Dearsley and Frank Rogers

Tick the correct answer.

1 Mrs. Smith wanted a new pet because

a) her budgie had died. ☐ **b)** she wanted a more exciting pet. ☐

2 Mrs. Smith had to make

a) a large pond in the garden. ☐ **b)** a large cage in the garden. ☐

3 Crocodiles

a) make good, friendly pets. ☐ **b)** have nasty habits. ☐

4 One day, a cat came

a) into the garden. ☐ **b)** into the house. ☐

5 The crocodile

a) ate the cat. ☐ **b)** chased the cat. ☐

6 Mrs. Smith said

a) the cat had gone indoors. ☐ **b)** sorry to the lady next door. ☐

Name ________________________ Date ______________

Archie the Ugly Dinosaur

Archie was a very small dinosaur, much smaller than all his friends. He couldn't keep up and he was usually in the way.

Then Archie woke up one morning and *felt* he was growing at last. But when he looked down at himself, he was covered all over in little spikes!

Everyone laughed when they saw him. They laughed so much that Archie ran away, deep into the forest.

When Archie had gone, the big dinosaurs began blaming each other.

"You shouldn't have laughed at him," said Triceratops.

"Well, you laughed first," cried Stegosaurus.

Diplodocus was thoughtful. "The forest is a dangerous place for a small dinosaur," she said. "We'd better find him before the big Rexes do."

They began to look at once. They searched by day, and they searched by night. They came to the mountains where the big Rexes lived.

"I don't like it here," Triceratops whispered.

From *Archie the Ugly Dinosaur* by M. Christine Butler

These six pictures show the story of Archie.

1

____

____

2

____

____

3

____

____

4

____

____

5

____

____

6

____

____

Copy each of these sentences under the correct picture.

Everyone laughed at him.
The other dinosaurs began to search for him.
Archie ran into the forest.
They came to the mountains where the big Rexes lived.
Archie the small dinosaur woke up.
He saw that he was covered in little spikes.

Name ______________________ Date ______________

Betsy and Bop

Rodri has two rabbits. One is called Betsy and one is called Bop. Betsy is white and Bop is black. Betsy and Bop live in a hutch in the garden. Rodri changes their water and feeds them every day. Their favourite foods are carrots and lettuce. Every week Rodri cleans out their hutch and gives them fresh clean hay to sleep on. In the summer they are allowed to run in the garden. Rodri likes to stroke them because their fur is so soft.

Finish the sentences.

1 The rabbits are called B ______ and B ______ .

2 Betsy is a white rabbit and Bop is a ________ rabbit.

3 Betsy and Bop live in a ________ in the garden.

4 Their favourite foods are ________ and ________ .

5 Rodri likes to ________ them because their fur is so soft.

Can you draw a picture for each of these sentences?

6 Bop is a black rabbit and Betsy is a white rabbit.

7 Rodri gives them carrots and lettuce.

8 The rabbits live in a hutch.

Name ________________________________ Date ________________

Adam's New Pet

"I'm up!" called Adam, as he jumped out of bed and ran into his Mum's and Dad's bedroom. He pulled the curtains and jumped on to the bed. Mum and Dad were slowly waking up.

"Come on, it's my birthday. I'm seven!"

"Yes," Dad mumbled. "But it's only six o'clock. Does your birthday have to start so early?"

They all went downstairs where Adam found several cards and some interesting parcels waiting for him.

Adam soon had sweets, books, felt-tipped pens and a football all piled up. A new football kit from his Nan and Grandad was a big surprise. Then Dad went into the kitchen and came out carrying a cardboard box. It had holes in the top and strange scuffling sounds came from inside. Adam opened it and there was a tiny black-and-white puppy. He carefully reached in and lifted out the soft furry animal. He cuddled it gently and then said, "Hello, Sam. I've always wanted a pet of my own."

Answer these questions in sentences.

1 How old was Adam?

____

2 Who didn't want to get up so early?

____

3 Who sent Adam a new football kit?

____

4 What was Dad holding when he came in from the kitchen?

____

5 What sound was coming from the box?

____

6 What was in the box?

____

7 What did Adam do when he lifted the puppy out?

____

8 What name did he give the puppy?

____

9 Cut out the pictures below and arrange them in the correct order, or write 1, 2, 3 or 4 under each picture to show the correct order.

Name ______________________ Date ______________

Flip and Flop

Chris and Peter sat watching the two furry creatures very carefully. Six weeks ago, on their seventh birthday, Mum and Dad had given them two brown hamsters in a roomy cage.

The cage was very comfortable, with a water bottle and feeding dishes on the floor. A ladder led to the top floor where warm, fluffy bedding gave the hamsters a cosy, dark place to curl up and sleep during the day.

Chris called his hamster Flip because it was very lively and loved doing acrobatics up the ladder and along the bars of the cage. Peter's hamster was called Flop because it was not good at climbing and kept rolling down the ladder!

Dad had given the twins an old piece of wood and on it they had made an adventure playground for their hamsters with a wall of LEGO bricks around it. They had made tunnels from cardboard tubes and hills from crumpled paper.

Flip and Flop loved special treats of apple and bits of biscuit, so Chris and Peter hid some of these inside the tubes and under the hills for the hamsters to find.

True or false?
In your book, copy out the sentences which are true.

1 Chris and Peter are friends.
2 Chris and Peter are twins.
3 They are seven years old.
4 They are six years old.
5 Flip and Flop are mice.
6 Flip and Flop are hamsters.

Now answer these questions in sentences.
Write the answers in your book.

7 How long have the twins had their hamsters?
8 Why does Chris call his hamster Flip?
9 What did Chris and Peter make for their hamsters?
10 What special treats do the hamsters like to eat?

Name ______________________ Date ______________

A Letter to Gran and Grandad

14, Hollywell Road,
Bensley,
Wiltshire
BN2 4SY
Monday 11th October

Dear Gran and Grandad,

Thank you ever so much for the jigsaw and the new jeans that you sent me for my birthday.

I was sorry that you and Grandad couldn't come over on my birthday last Thursday. I hope that Grandad's leg is better now and that you'll be able to visit us soon.

I really enjoyed my birthday. Mum and Dad gave me a new pair of rollerblades, Andrew gave me a new pencilcase full of pens and pencils and I had some books and sweets. I also had some money from Auntie Linda. My class sang 'Happy Birthday' to me and Mum made me a lovely cake. It was pink with eight coloured balloons on it, with a candle stuck in each balloon.

Instead of a party I was allowed to choose four friends to take out on Saturday. I invited Amy, Holly, Angela and Katy. We went ice skating and then to McDonalds afterwards. We had burgers and lovely, thick banana milkshakes. We had a great time. See you soon.

With love from Nicola xxxx

Read the letter carefully and then answer these questions in sentences. Write the answers in your book.

1. Who was the letter to?
2. Who wrote the letter?
3. What did Gran and Grandad send Nicola for her birthday?
4. Why couldn't Gran and Grandad visit Nicola on her birthday?
5. On which day and date was Nicola's birthday?
6. How old was Nicola?
7. Who did Nicola take on her birthday treat?
8. Where did they go?
9. What did they have to eat?
10. Draw and label six of the presents that Nicola received for her birthday.

Name ______________________ Date ______________

Come to my Party

Dear Samara,

Please come to my birthday party
on Saturday 4th May
at McDonalds, North Street, Newford.
We will be going swimming first at the Leisure Centre.
We will leave my house at 2p.m. and be back by 6p.m.
PLEASE LET ME KNOW IF YOU CAN COME.

I am 8

From

Jason

12 Lakeside Road,
Newford

Answer these questions in sentences.
Write the answers in your book.

1 Who is having a birthday party?
2 Where will the party be held?
3 What other treat will there be?
4 What will Samara need to take with her?
5 On which day will the party be held?
6 Where must Samara be by 2p.m.?
7 How long will Samara spend with Jason?
8 How old will Jason be?

Name ______________________ Date ______________

Sailor Sam

Now Sam he was a sailor,
He sailed the seven seas,
He was at home on any ship,
In gale or wind or breeze.

Now as he went a-sailing,
Across the ocean deep,
A storm blew up. "Ahoy!" he cried,
"How this old ship do creak!"

The poor old ship, it tossed and rolled,
Among the giant waves,
Although the sailors clung on tight
Some went to watery graves.

Now Sailor Sam was lucky,
He drifted mile on mile,
And then the ocean threw him up
On a pleasant desert isle.

He made himself a shelter,
Of twigs and leaves and bark,
And lit himself a cosy fire,
For he did not like the dark!

Although he's made a home there,
He always is alone,
And his message in a bottle says,
"I'd like to get back home."

Sue Dillon

1 Copy this list of words into your book. Then find the words in the poem that rhyme with them. The first one is done for you.

seas – breeze
waves
mile
bark

2 Read the poem carefully, and then write these sentences in the correct order. There is one sentence for each verse. Draw a picture for each sentence, making sure you put in all the details described in the verse.

Sam lit a fire outside his new home.

A dreadful storm blew up.

Sam was shipwrecked on an island.

Sam has sent a message in a bottle in the hope that he'll be rescued.

Sam was a very good sailor.

The ship was tossed about and some sailors were drowned.

Name ______________________ Date ______________

Kijo the Baby Gorilla

Kijo the baby gorilla lives in the big dark African forest. When his mother goes looking for berries or fruit to eat, Kijo always goes with her. He clings tight to the thick fur on her back.

Kijo loves playing hide and seek with his brother and sister, round and round among the tall trees and the thick ferns. Life in the forest is fun!

While the young gorillas play, the father gorilla keeps watch. Suddenly he smells danger.

Men!

They are coming closer and closer, hunting for gorillas. Father beats his chest and roars.

Quick, quick, Kijo! Father gorilla races away with the little ones, into the thickest part of the forest, where the men cannot find them.

At last Kijo's father decides it is safe to stop. But Kijo cannot see his mother anywhere. Where is she? What will he do without the warm comfort of her fur? Kijo creeps off to look for his lost mother.

From *Kijo the Baby Gorilla* by Jill Jago and Gerry Livingstone

---

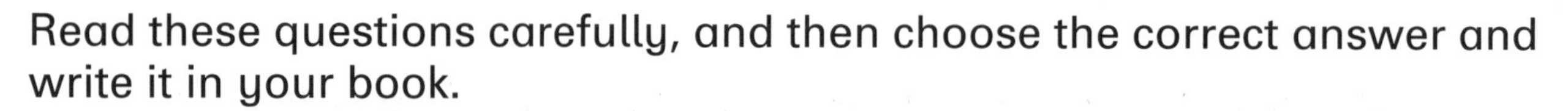

Read these questions carefully, and then choose the correct answer and write it in your book.

1 Where does Kijo live?
- **a)** Kijo lives in the African forest.
- **b)** Kijo lives in a cave.

2 Who does Kijo go with to find fruit and berries?
- **a)** Kijo looks for fruit and berries on his own.
- **b)** Kijo goes with his mother to find fruit and berries.

3 How many brothers and sisters does Kijo have?
- **a)** Kijo does not have any brothers or sisters.
- **b)** Kijo has a brother and a sister.

4 What is father gorilla frightened of?
- **a)** He is frightened of men.
- **b)** He is frightened of a lion.

5 Who takes the small gorillas deep into the forest?
- **a)** Kijo's mother takes them deep into the forest.
- **b)** Kijo's father takes them deep into the forest.

6 Draw a picture of Kijo deep in the dark African forest.

Name ______________________ Date ______________

The Giant Sunflower Competition

Class 3D are having a competition to see who can grow the tallest sunflower. This is what their teacher tells the children to do:

"We must buy a packet of seeds, some 9cm pots and a sack of compost from the garden centre. Each pot must be filled with the compost. Then each sunflower seed can be pushed down in the middle of the pot, about 2cm into the compost. Make sure the seed is covered and press the surface of the compost down gently. Water well and add a little more compost if the level drops. Put the pot in a place where it is warm and there is plenty of daylight. When the compost feels dry on the surface, water it carefully but do not let the pot stand in water. In a week or two the seed should sprout. When the plants are about 10cm tall we can plant them at the back of the school flowerbeds, against the wall which will give them support. You can put a plastic label with your name on it next to your plant. You must water them well and then we'll see whose sunflower grows the tallest."

Read the passage again carefully, and then make a list of instructions on "How to grow a sunflower". First, list the things that you will need.

Name ______________________ Date ______________

Gorillas

Gorillas are the biggest of the apes. They live in Africa, in groups in the forest. A fully-grown gorilla can be bigger than a man.

They are usually gentle animals but they sometimes get angry. A gorilla roars and beats his chest to frighten an enemy.

The gorilla has a hairy, dark-brown coat. The mountain gorilla has a thicker coat to keep him warm, as the mountains can be cold and damp.

Gorillas eat plants and fruit; they spend their days eating, resting and playing. They sleep high in the trees in a sort of nest they build from branches and leaves. Gorillas can walk on the forest floor or climb and swing through the trees.

True or false? In your book, copy out the sentences which are true.

1. Gorillas eat plants and fruit.
2. Gorillas are fierce creatures.
3. Gorillas spend their days hunting other animals.
4. They live in Africa.
5. Gorillas spend their days eating, resting and fighting.
6. They sleep high in the trees in nests made of branches and leaves.
7. The high mountains in Africa can be cold and damp.
8. Chimpanzees are the biggest of the apes.
9. The gorilla beats his chest and roars when he is angry.
10. Gorillas are good climbers.

Name ______________________________ Date ______________

Favourite Foods

Read these passages.

Naresh
I love pizza, salad, yogurt and all sorts of fruit.
I don't really like meat, and ice cream makes my teeth hurt!

Holly
I am a vegetarian. I eat lots of vegetables, salad, cheese and eggs.
I love yogurt, fruit and ice cream.

Daniel
My favourites are roast dinners, burgers and chips, ice cream and yogurt.
I don't like vegetables or fruit or cheese.

Saria
I love all kinds of meat and chips.
I don't like cheese. I eat anything sweet or fruity.

Fill in the grid by putting a ✓ if the child likes the food and a ✗ if he or she does not.

	Naresh	Daniel	Holly	Saria
Cheese and tomato pizza				
Roast meat				
Burger and chips				
Ice cream				
Fruit				
Yogurt				

Answer these questions in sentences.
Write the answers in your book.

1 Which child is a vegetarian?
2 Which children like meat?
3 Which sweet food do all four children like?
4 Which children like cheese?
5 How many children like vegetables?
6 Which children would enjoy a meal of burgers, chips and ice cream?
7 Vegetables and fruit are very good for you. Who doesn't include these in his or her diet?
8 Write a menu to plan your favourite meal.

Name ________________________ Date ______________

Susie the Spider

Susie was a spider,
She wove a silken web,
In a high, dark corner,
Of Mr. Harpin's shed.

Mr. Harpin didn't mind,
He left her quite alone,
Provided that, into his house,
She'd never, ever roam.

Her eight long legs she put to work,
They were a little hairy,
Scuttling here, scuttling there,
Made Susie rather scary!

Every day she feasted,
On careless flies that flew,
Into her web so sticky,
So Susie grew and grew!

Then from her nest, one summer day,
Came spiderlings galore,
"Oh, no," said Mr. Harpin,
"I don't want any more!"

By Sue and Terry Dillon

Answer these questions in sentences.
Write the answers in your book.

1 Where did Susie live?
2 What was her web like?
3 What did Mr. Harpin feel about Susie?
4 Where didn't he want Susie to go?
5 How many legs does a spider have?
6 What did Susie eat?
7 How did she catch her food?
8 What appeared from her nest one day?
9 What line in the poem tells you that Susie was good at catching food?
10 What made Susie so scary?

Name _______________ Date _______________

The Legend of Rome

Roman boys and girls were told a legend about how the city of Rome was built.

Romulus and Remus were twins and they were also royal princes. When they were babies they were placed in a basket on the River Tiber by their wicked uncle. He hoped they would die so that he could become ruler, but they were rescued by a she-wolf who heard their cries. She fed the babies with her own milk and cared for them. When they grew into boys they were found and taken in by a shepherd, Faustulus, and his wife. Discovering who they really were, Romulus and Remus went on to build the city of Rome. The two young brothers argued with each other about who should be king and Romulus killed Remus. Romulus became the first King of Rome in 753BC.

With reference to *What do we Know about the Romans?* by Mike Corbishley

---

Read the story carefully and then write these sentences in your book. Put in the words that are missing, so that the sentences make sense. All the words you need can be found in the story.

1 The twins were called _______ and _______.

2 They were royal _______.

3 Their wicked _______ wanted to become ruler instead of them.

4 He told his servants to put them in a _______ on the River Tiber.

5 Their uncle hoped that the babies would _______.

6 A she-wolf _______ them.

7 She _______ the babies and _______ for them.

8 Later on, the boys were found by a _______ called Faustulus.

9 The shepherd and his _______ looked after the boys.

10 Romulus and Remus discovered they were princes and decided to build a _______.

11 They argued about who should be _______.

12 Romulus killed _______ and became the first King of Rome.

Name ______________________________ Date ______________

Penguins

Most penguins make nests of small pebbles in which they lay two eggs, but the largest penguin, the emperor penguin, does not make a nest at all. Instead, the female lays an egg on the ice in the middle of winter. The male immediately scoops it up on to his feet and lowers a flap of skin over it, so that his body can keep the egg warm until it hatches. Then both parents busy themselves bringing back small fish to feed the single chick. There is not enough room for two eggs on the male's feet, so the female emperor penguin lays only one.

From *Polar Regions* by Nigel Bonner

Choose the correct sentence from each pair and write it in your book.

1 **a)** Penguins make nests of twigs and grasses.
b) Most penguins make nests of pebbles.

2 **a)** Most penguins lay two eggs.
b) Most penguins lay one egg.

3 **a)** The emperor penguin is the largest type of penguin.
b) The emperor penguin is the smallest type of penguin.

4 **a)** A female emperor penguin lays three eggs.
b) A female emperor penguin lays one egg.

5 **a)** The female emperor penguin lays her egg on the ice in spring.
b) The female emperor penguin lays her egg on the ice in winter.

6 **a)** The male emperor penguin keeps the egg warm on his feet.
b) The female emperor penguin keeps her egg in a nest.

7 **a)** The female lays only one egg because they can't feed more.
b) The female lays only one egg because there is no room on the male's feet for more.

8 **a)** The female emperor penguin brings back fish for the chick.
b) Both parents bring back fish for the chick.

Name ______________________ Date ______________

The Birth of Jesus

Mary and Joseph were looking forward to the ___1___ of their baby. Joseph was a carpenter and had to make a ___2___ for the baby.

One ___3___ a messenger arrived from the Emperor Augustus who had given the ___4___ that everyone had to go back to the town where they were born in order to be ___5___ . Joseph was ___6___ about Mary because such a ___7___ journey would not be ___8___ for her, but they had to ___9___ .

Mary travelled on a ___10___ to Bethlehem and when they got there they could only find a stable to ___11___ in. Mary had her ___12___ that night. She wrapped him up and put him down to ___13___.

Shepherds and wise men followed a ___14___ which guided them to the ___15___. They brought ___16___ for the baby.

---

1 Some of the words have been missed out of this well-known story. For each number, write a word which would fill the gap.

1	______	9	______
2	______	10	______
3	______	11	______
4	______	12	______
5	______	13	______
6	______	14	______
7	______	15	______
8	______	16	______

2 Now draw a picture about the story in your book.

Name ______________________________ Date ______________

Good to Eat

Jason, Sarah and Rebecca were busy helping Mrs. Patel in her garden. She lived next door and the children enjoyed working on her vegetable plot.

The children's Mum and Dad had a very ordinary garden with grass and bushes and flowers and the children were not allowed to dig there. But Mrs. Patel's plot was so much more interesting. She grew tomatoes, peppers and cucumbers in her greenhouse and shared them with her neighbours. The children helped her dig the soil to plant her beans, carrots, onions and potatoes. She had neat rows of frilly green lettuces, and bright red radishes too.

Today Mrs. Patel was digging up some potatoes and carrots and picking some tomatoes and beans for a special reason. Tomorrow the Harvest Festival would be held at St. Mary's School. Sarah had written a Harvest Prayer thanking God for a good harvest of fruit and vegetables, and she was going to read it during the Harvest Festival celebrations. Jason and Rebecca had covered two boxes with green paper ready to put Mrs. Patel's vegetables in. They had invited Mrs. Patel to the celebration at school and she was looking forward to it. She liked to hear the children singing and was interested to see the great display in the hall. Some of the fruit and vegetables were home-grown, but some came from the greengrocer and had been grown in hot countries far away.

Afterwards, all the fruit and vegetables that were given by the children were taken to the old people's home nearby, where the old people not only enjoyed the food but also liked having the children come and visit them.

Choose the correct ending to each sentence.
Write the sentence in your book.

1 Jason, Sarah and Rebecca helped Mrs. Patel
a) in her garden. **b)** with her shopping.

2 Mrs. Patel grew
a) many vegetables. **b)** trees and flowers.

3 She grew beans, carrots, onions and potatoes
a) in her greenhouse. **b)** in her vegetable plot.

4 Vegetables were being collected
a) for supper. **b)** to take to the Harvest Festival.

5 Sarah had written
a) a Harvest Prayer. **b)** a story about a Harvest Festival.

6 A Harvest Festival celebration was being held at
a) St. Mary's Church. **b)** St. Mary's School.

7 Mrs. Patel was invited to
a) the Harvest Festival celebrations at school. **b)** the old people's home.

8 The fruit and vegetables were
a) sent to other countries. **b)** taken to the old people's home nearby.

9 Draw a box of fruit and vegetables that would help make an attractive Harvest Festival display.

Name ______________________ Date ______________

The Jolly Witch

Mrs. Jolly was the school caretaker. She had a short nose and two comfy round chins, and curly brown hair, going grey. Mrs. Jolly had a ginger cat. Mrs. Jolly was friendly, nice and cuddly.

But there was something the headmistress didn't know. Or the other teachers. Or the children. In the Autumn Term when Mrs. Jolly swept the playground clear of leaves with a broomstick, even then, nobody guessed that she was… a witch!

At the end of school each day when everyone had gone home, Mrs. Jolly the caretaker became Mrs. Jolly the witch. This was the time when she used her magic powers, though she looked just the same. Friendly and cuddly.

Mrs. Jolly used her powers very sensibly. She made them work for her. "To save my legs," she said.

For Mrs. Jolly had to clean the whole school, all three classrooms and the hall. She took her vacuum cleaner, her dustpan and brush and her dusters into

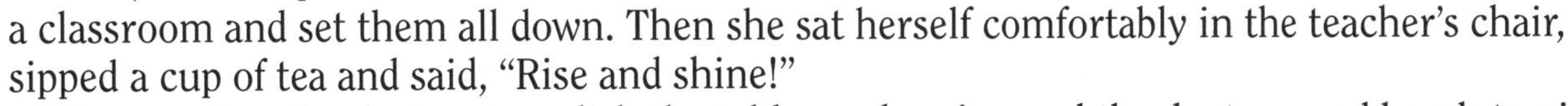

a classroom and set them all down. Then she sat herself comfortably in the teacher's chair, sipped a cup of tea and said, "Rise and shine!"

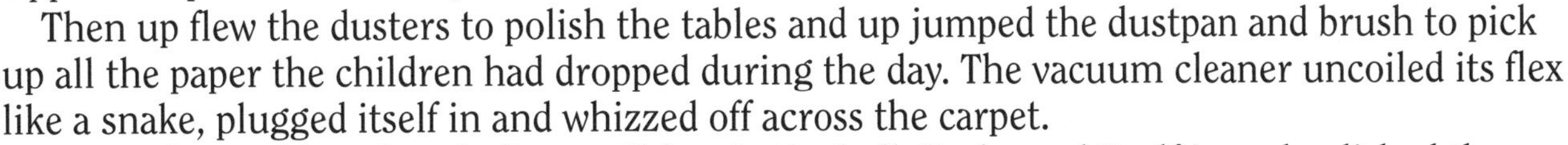

Then up flew the dusters to polish the tables and up jumped the dustpan and brush to pick up all the paper the children had dropped during the day. The vacuum cleaner uncoiled its flex like a snake, plugged itself in and whizzed off across the carpet.

Mrs. Jolly used her electric floor polisher in the hall. It plugged itself in and polished the floor until it shone. And it goes without saying that when all the rooms had been cleaned, the curtains drew themselves and all the lights switched themselves off!

The only work that Mrs. Jolly did herself was in the autumn when she swept the playground clear of leaves. Out there in the open, there was a risk that people in the village might catch sight of a large broomstick sweeping up the leaves. All by itself.

From *The Jolly Witch* by Dick King-Smith

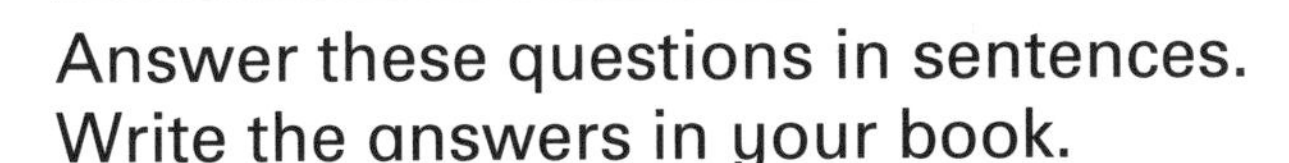

Answer these questions in sentences.
Write the answers in your book.

1. What was Mrs. Jolly's job?
2. What sort of person was Mrs. Jolly?
3. Did Mrs. Jolly have any pets?
4. When did Mrs. Jolly become a witch?
5. How did she get all her jobs done?
6. What were her magic words?
7. What were Mrs. Jolly's jobs?
8. Was Mrs. Jolly a wicked witch?
9. What did Mrs. Jolly do while all the work was being done?
10. What did the curtains and lights do?
11. What was the only work that Mrs. Jolly did herself?
12. Why did she sweep the playground herself?

Name ______________________ Date ______________

Alice Alone

Alice's and Scooter's mother had been ill with flu. Just as she got better, Father became ill – and it was then that Grandpa came to the rescue. He drove to the house in his old red pick-up truck, and said that he would take Alice and Scooter to his farm for a few days.

The farm was small, and high up on the moors. Grandpa had lived there ever since he was a small boy. He said that he would never leave it. Even when Grandmother died, he wouldn't consider leaving. He said that towns made him feel as though he was in prison. He would stay where he was, with his sheep and hens, and where he could see the moors and sky all around him. Mrs. Hammond came from the village each day, and cleaned the house for him and cooked his food. It was, said Grandpa, a good arrangement.

Alice thought that going to stay with Grandpa was a good arrangement. It was winter, and she had never seen the farm in winter-time. But Alice's mother wasn't too sure about Grandpa's plan. "Will you be able to manage with two children?" she said.

"Of course I'll manage!" said Grandpa – and he went upstairs, to help Alice and Scooter to pack. He bundled everything into the bags – jeans and shirts, sweaters and socks, and Scooter's stuffed toy kangaroo called Booker. No one knew why Scooter loved Booker so much – or why he called him Booker – for he was old and battered, and had lost his squeak and one ear. But Scooter wouldn't go anywhere without him.

Scooter's real name was James, but he ran about so quickly that everybody called him Scooter. Now, with his bag banging against his knees, he ran down the path to the red pick-up truck.

Alice stayed behind for a moment, to say goodbye to her mother. "It really is a good arrangement!" she said. Then she ran to join Scooter and Grandpa.

From *Alice Alone* by Shirley Isherwood

Answer these questions in sentences.
Write the answers in your book.

1. Why were Alice and Scooter going to stay with Grandpa?
2. Where did Grandpa live?
3. How did they get to Grandpa's farm?
4. Give two reasons why Grandpa wouldn't move.
5. Did Grandpa cook and clean for himself?
6. Make a list of what Grandpa packed for the children to take with them.
7. Why did Alice particularly want to stay at the farm?
8. What was Booker and what did he look like?
9. What was Scooter's real name?
10. Why was he called Scooter?

Name ______________________ Date ______________

A Storm in a Lunchbox

Sally couldn't wait until lunch-time. For a treat, Mum had put a very special yogurt in her lunchbox. It was the kind that had two parts, one with yogurt and one with fruit. When you were ready to eat it, you tipped one into the other. She had a strawberry one, and that was her favourite.

At playtime all the children went out to play but Sally had to stay in for a few minutes to finish off her work. As soon as it was done she went to the shelf where the lunchboxes were kept to get out her apple to eat in the playground. She opened her box, took out the apple and stopped – a packet of cheese sandwiches, a flask of drink – but the strawberry yogurt had gone! Sally felt angry and upset at the same time. How could anyone steal from her lunchbox? Quickly, she began opening all the other boxes. She was frightened because she knew that if Miss Brown caught her she would be in serious trouble, but someone had opened her box and taken her yogurt.

In the fifth box she opened, there it was, her special strawberry yogurt. Sally looked at the name on the box and couldn't believe her eyes – Emily, her very best friend! Sally did not know what to do. Should she go and tell Miss Brown that Emily was a thief? Should she go and find Emily and tell her how horrible she was? No. Sally picked up the yogurt and put it back in her box where it belonged. She remembered she had told Emily about it on the way to school that morning and Emily had said that it was her favourite too.

When she went into the playground Emily was waiting for her.

"What shall we play?" said Emily.

"Go away," Sally shouted. "I don't want to play with you!"

"Why?" said Emily.

"You know why," shouted Sally." I hate you. I don't want to be your friend any more!"

Emily ran away crying.

"Good," thought Sally." Serves her right. That will teach her to steal."

When lunch-time came, Sally ate her sandwiches and then her special strawberry yogurt. Emily was crying and the dinner ladies were fussing around her, but Sally went off by herself.

It was art that afternoon. Sally painted a picture of a fireman.

"Had a good day, dear?" said her Mum when Sally got home.

Sally smiled and nodded.

"I bet you are hungry, aren't you?" asked Mum. "You left your yogurt on the kitchen table. What a silly girl!"

Sally just stared at her Mum. What had she done?

Answer these questions in sentences.
Write the answers in your book.

1. Why was Sally looking forward to lunch-time?
2. Why didn't she go out to play on time?
3. What had Sally brought to eat at playtime?
4. Where were the lunchboxes kept?
5. What did she do when she discovered that her yogurt had gone?
6. Why was Sally so shocked to find the yogurt in Emily's lunchbox?
7. What did Sally decide to do?
8. Why was Sally pleased when she made Emily cry in the playground?
9. Why did Mum think Sally would be hungry?
10. Write down five words that describe how Sally felt when she realised her mistake.

Name ______________________ Date ______________

The Selfish Giant

Every afternoon, as they were coming home from school, the children used to go and play in the Giant's garden.

It was a large, lovely garden, with soft green grass. Here and there over the grass stood beautiful flowers like stars, and there were twelve peach trees that in the springtime broke out into delicate blossoms of pink and pearl, and in the autumn bore rich fruit. The birds sat on the trees and sang so sweetly that the children used to stop their games in order to listen to them.

"How happy we are here!" they cried to each other.

One day the Giant came back. He had been to visit his friend the Cornish Ogre, and had stayed with him for seven years. After the seven years were over he had said all that he had to say, for his conversation was limited, and he was determined to return to his own castle. When he arrived he saw the children playing in the garden.

"What are you doing here?" he cried in a very gruff voice, and the children ran away. "My own garden is my own garden," said the Giant. "Anyone can understand that, and I will allow nobody to play in it but myself."

So he built a high wall all round it, and put up a noticeboard:

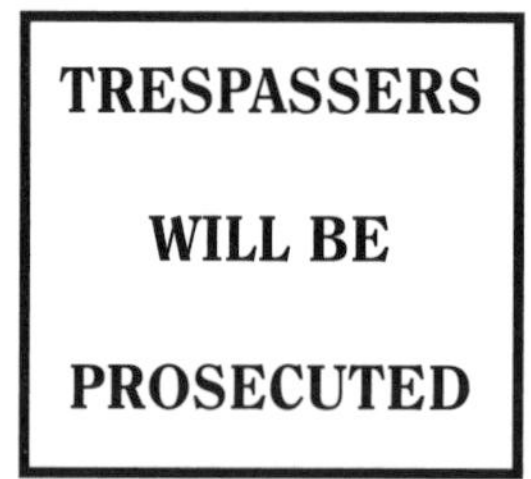

He was a very selfish Giant.

From *The Selfish Giant* by Oscar Wilde

True or false?
In your book, copy out the sentences which are true.

1. The children loved to play in the Giant's garden.
2. They played there each morning.
3. Green grass and beautiful flowers grew there.
4. Twelve peach trees blossomed there in the autumn.
5. The children liked to listen to the birds singing.
6. The Giant had been away for ten years.
7. He had stayed with his friend the Cornish Ogre.
8. The Giant came back because they had nothing else to talk about.
9. The Giant said no one else could play in his garden.
10. The children were frightened and ran away.
11. He put up a sign saying "Trespassers will be eaten".
12. The Giant thought only of himself.
13. Draw a picture to illustrate the story.

Name ______________________ Date ______________

The Trouble with Mice

Mary is supposed to be looking after her brother's pet mouse while he is away. But one day something awful happens.

It can't be, thinks Mary. She stares in disbelief. For a second she cannot move. She closes her eyes and opens them again, hoping she is wrong. But she's not. The door of Mickey's cage is open. I shut it properly, I'm sure I shut it properly, she thinks. But she can't remember exactly.

She slams the shed door shut and rushes over to the cage. "Mickey! Mickey!" Any minute now his twitching pink nose will appear. Any minute now.

"Mickey! Mickey!" She peers into the cage, reaches her hand through the door, turning over the shavings. Then she lifts out the jam jar and tips it out, pulling with her fingers at the bedding. There are seeds and shreds of lettuce and droppings: but no Mickey.

The worst has happened. She has let Mickey escape. No, she thinks, the worst hasn't happened. The worst will happen on Friday when Chris gets back.

She stands, shoulders hunched, hands clasped to her mouth. Please God, let me find him. Please!

"You were a long time," says Mum.

"I was cleaning the cage up a bit."

"Then you wash those hands this minute."

Mary keeps returning to the shed where she thinks she sees a little ear poking out over a flowerpot, or a little tail from behind a watering can. But it is only a scrap of paper, or a piece of wire. She starts to see mice everywhere. She worries about treading on Mickey, and she walks with her head down, staring at the ground.

"What's the matter with you?" asks Mum. "You've a face like a week of wet Sundays. Have you been quarrelling with Anna again?"

It is when she is coming back from the corner shop with the loaf of bread Mum sent her for, that she decides what to do. She runs towards the pet shop. She can't take too long or Mum will start to worry.

From *The Trouble with Mice* by Pat Moore

Answer these questions in sentences.
Write the answers in your book.

1 Who does Mickey the mouse belong to?
2 Why is Mary looking after him?
3 Why does Mary close her eyes and hope she is wrong?
4 How has Mickey escaped?
5 What does Mary expect to appear when she calls him?
6 Where does Mary look in the cage?
7 Why is Mary dreading Friday?
8 Why does Mum tell Mary to wash her hands?
9 Why do you think Mary doesn't tell Mum what has happened?
10 Why does Mary keep going back to the shed?
11 Why does Mary keep looking at the ground?
12 Why do you think Mary decides to go to the pet shop?

Name ______________________________ Date ______________

Emily's Legs

He pulled back on the thread on which Emily was standing.

"Get lost!" he said, and let it go with a twang.

Emily was hurled from the web like a stone from a catapult. At the same time the room was filled with a sudden roaring noise, a noise that grew louder as Emily fell until, as she hit the floor, it was very loud indeed. And very close.

Dazed and helpless, Emily could only watch as the monster rushed towards her. Her mother's words echoed in her brain. "The hoover will get you!"

A happy ending was the last thing Emily expected when she was sucked into the mouth of the vacuum cleaner. The first thing she felt was a sharp pain (two sharp pains, to be exact). Then she found herself in thick, choking blackness, unable to see or cry out – for her eyes and mouth were full of dust – and unable to hear anything but the dreadful, deafening noise of the machine. For a moment, Emily thought she was dead.

But then the hoover was switched off, the heap of fluff and dirt settled to the bottom of the bag, and Emily fought her way to the top of it. To her surprise and relief she found she was not alone, for suddenly a voice rang out in the darkness. "All clear, my lads!" it cried. "Us can unroll now."

Once her eyes had grown accustomed to the darkness, Emily could see that the speaker was a large woodlouse, and that several other woodlice had climbed to the top of the pile of dust. They looked at Emily in a friendly manner.

From *Emily's Legs* by Dick King-Smith

Answer these questions in sentences.
Write the answers in your book.

1. How did Emily come to be on the floor?
2. What did Emily hear as she hit the floor?
3. How did she know what it was?
4. Why couldn't Emily escape from the hoover?
5. Which group of words tell you that Emily didn't think she'd escape?
6. Was Emily hurt in any way?
7. Why couldn't Emily see or shout for help?
8. What did Emily do when the hoover was switched off?
9. Who did Emily meet in the hoover bag?
10. Which sentence tells you that the woodlice wouldn't hurt Emily?

Name ______________________________ Date ______________

A Bear called Bamboo

On her eighth birthday, Charlotte went to the zoo with her friend Laura. They loved all the different bears: the white polar bear from the cold north lands, the big brown bear which was most like a teddy bear; but best of all they loved the panda. Dad bought Charlotte a cuddly panda to take home. He suggested she should call it Bamboo and when Charlotte asked why, Dad gave her a book on animals so that she could find out.

A panda is a large animal related to the bear family. It is as tall and as heavy as a large human being, and it has black-and-white fur. Its head, neck, back and stomach are white with black eyes, ears, arms and legs.

The panda lives in the mountains of China where it is cold and wet for many months of the year. Its furry coat helps to keep it warm. The panda eats one main food – bamboo. Luckily, the panda can find great forests of bamboo plants on the mountainsides and it eats huge amounts every day. It spends most of the day eating and the rest of the time sleeping.

It has sharp claws to help it to climb trees, but it can move well on the ground, too. The panda is not a friendly creature. It likes to be by itself, so few baby pandas are born. When a baby is born it is tiny, only about the size and weight of an orange. Its mother must look after it carefully to help it to survive.

There may be only about 1,000 pandas left in China because, although hunting pandas is against the law, there is another big danger. The huge bamboo forests where the panda lives are found only in one part of China, but people have cleared parts of these forests for more farmland and to build villages. This means that the panda has a smaller area to live and feed in, and some have starved to death. Now people in China are setting up areas where hungry pandas can be protected and fed.

Answer these questions in sentences.
Write the answers in your book.

1. Where did Charlotte go on her birthday?
2. Why did Dad give Charlotte a book about animals?
3. Which parts of the panda are black?
4. Which country does the panda come from?
5. What is the weather like in the place that the panda comes from?
6. What does the panda eat?
7. How does the panda spend its day?
8. What helps it to climb trees?
9. Why are there so few baby pandas?
10. Why are there so few pandas left?

Name ______________________ Date ______________

Swimming Pool Rules

Read the following and decide which are suitable rules for the use of the swimming pool.

- The pool is often crowded
- No snorkels
- Think of others
- Don't go out of your depth
- Children like swimming
- Never run on the poolside
- Some children wear armbands
- Swimming hats must be worn
- The water is very warm
- Don't shout or scream
- Don't pull anyone underwater
- No food or drink permitted at the poolside
- There are large changing rooms
- No smoking

Write the "Rules for the Pool" in your book.

Now design three signs that could be displayed around the pool to advertise these rules.

Name ______________________ Date ______________

Animal Antics Theme Park

IS IT AN ADVENTURE PLAYGROUND? IS IT A ZOO? IS IT A SUPER FAIRGROUND? IT'S ALL THREE!!!

Snakes and Ladders – prove your skills by go-karting on Britain's bendiest race track.

Black Bat Ride – don't close your eyes as the Black Bat takes you through the fearsome forest to his haunted house. No ghost train has ever been so scary!

Monkey Playground – climb, swing and slide through a monkey's paradise.

Cyclone Spider Ride – climb into a web on the spider's leg and hang on as you spin and twist.

Wally the Whale – sends you leaping and diving on the greatest watersplash ride ever.

Eliza the Elephant – will take you on a train ride around the whole park, with stops for you to go on your favourite rides.

Gerry the Giraffe – it's worth climbing the 53 steps to Gerry's head for the amazing helter-skelter ride down!

The Great Grizzly Bear – will you dare to ride this rollercoaster? Hang on for the ride of your life!

Come and join Rachel and Robbie the rabbits at *Pets' Corner.* Meet their friends the guinea pigs, the ducklings, Peter the Parrot and many others.

The Zebra Crossing Gift Ship *Patrick the Polar Bear's Ice Cream Parlour*

Caroline the Camel's Cosy Café – self-service – hot and cold snacks at reasonable prices

Petra the Panda's Pizza Place • Large picnic area • Toilet facilities include mother and baby rooms, wheelchair and pushchair access and facilities for the disabled

Animal Antics Theme Park

Lower Way, Otterford, Boxshire BX3 7EF

How to get here:

By car Exit the M77 at Junction 13. The theme park is well signposted.

By rail Alight at Otterford station, then take the regular minibus service to the theme park.

By bus Take the regular bus service service from Otterford – number 19 stops at the main entrance.

OPENING TIMES

Summer – 1st April – 31st October
Open daily 10a.m. – 6p.m.

Winter – 1st November – 31st March
Saturdays and Sundays only
10a.m. – 4p.m.
(excluding Christmas Day)

ADMISSION

	Summer	Winter
Adults	£7.00	£5.00
Children 3 to 16 years	£5.00	£3.00
Senior Citizens	£5.00	£3.00
Children under 3	free	free
Family Ticket (2 adults and 3 children)	£25	£15

Name ______________________ Date ____________

Animal Antics Theme Park *(continued)*

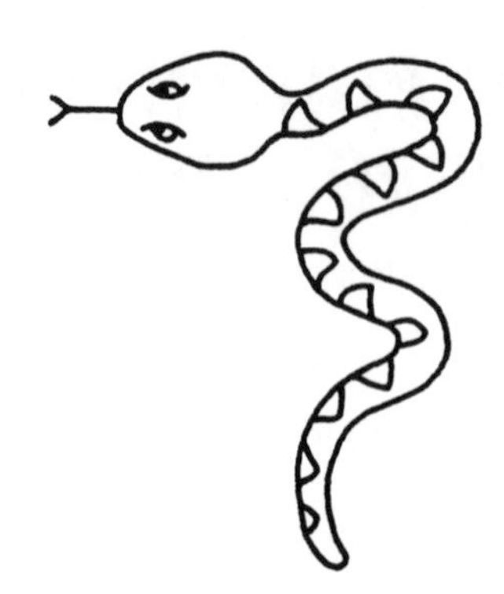

Answer these questions in sentences.
Write the answers in your book.

1. Which rides would you avoid if you didn't like heights?
2. How much would it cost Mr. and Mrs. Patel, Leela aged fifteen, Amil aged eight and Gita aged two to go to the theme park in November?
3. Sam is sixteen years old and he is taking his sister Kerri to the theme park as a treat for her ninth birthday in April. How much will it cost them to get in?
4. Chris is nine and his twin sisters are seven. Mum and Dad are going to take them to the theme park in August. How much will the admission cost?
5. James and Darren are very lively and are wearing Dad out. Which attraction will help them use up some of their energy?
6. Sui Ying loves slides. Which animal ride would she like best?
7. Where would Mr. and Mrs. Patel take their family for a pizza meal?
8. Mum and Chris want a hot meal but Dad and the twins want salad. Where would they go to eat?
9. On which day is the theme park closed in the winter season?
10. At what time does the theme park close in the summer?
11. Which ride would take you on a tour around the theme park?
12. Which activity can you take part in at Snakes Alive?
13. On which activity might you get very wet?
14. Which ride would you go on if you liked ghosts?

15. Design a poster on A4 paper to encourage people to visit the Animal Antics Theme Park. Try to include some detail about the rides and other information.

Name ______________________________ Date ______________

Waste Not, Want Not

Nicola and Daniel were up very early. Mum was surprised that she didn't have to keep calling them to get up.

"What's so exciting about today?" she asked.

"Gran and Grandad are letting us help clean out the shed, the garage, the spare room and the *loft!* They have such interesting old stuff stored away," Daniel explained.

Gran and Grandad always looked after the children at half-term, while Mum and Dad were at work.

Gran had said that it was time for a good spring-clean and that she wanted to clear out all the old junk before she started.

"Your Grandad keeps all sorts of old junk and rubbish," she grumbled. "This is a good chance to get rid of it. You two can help – but remember to wear old clothes, nothing fancy!"

When they arrived at Gran's they found Grandad with two huge, empty cardboard boxes and a lot of black sacks. "These," he explained, "are for sorting all the rubbish."

They started on the shed first. Nicola wondered why the rubbish had to be sorted; why not just put it in one huge pile? Grandad told her that even rubbish could be useful. Sorted into piles of glass, paper and metal it could be taken to the recycling bins in the supermarket car park.

"Then what?" Daniel wondered as he carefully put some glass bottles into a box.

Gran told them that, just as she saved old peelings, leftover food and kitchen rubbish to put on her compost heap to rot down and be used to improve the soil in the garden, so the rubbish put in the recycling bins could be used again. The old cola cans that Nicola was putting in a black sack would be melted down in a furnace and made into something new. The papers that Grandad was putting into a box would be mashed up and made into new paper. The glass would be ground up, melted and put into moulds to make new glass bottles and jars.

By the end of the day they were very tired but they had three huge piles of rubbish ready for the recycling bins. Grandad promised that the next day they would take it all to the recycling bins and then have lunch in the supermarket café.

"But," demanded Gran, "what about all this?" She pointed to a number of items on the lawn – an old bicycle, a broken rabbit hutch, a battered toy fort and an old pushchair. Grandad, Daniel and Nicola looked a bit guilty.

"Grandad said we could keep those," said the children. "He said we could mend them, paint them and play with them. After all, that's recycling too, isn't it?"

Answer these questions in sentences.
Write the answers in your book.

1. Why were Nicola and Daniel up so early?
2. Why did Gran and Grandad look after the children?
3. Why did Gran want to clear out all the rubbish?
4. To recycle means
   a) to buy a new bike.
   b) to re-use waste materials to make new things.
   c) to go back home on your bike.
5. Why do you think Daniel put the glass bottles in a box and not a plastic sack?
6. How is glass recycled?
7. How did they feel at the end of the day?
8. What plans did Grandad have for the next day?
9. What was Grandad going to help the children do with the things they had kept?
10. Draw three recycling bins (5cmx5cm) and label them with the three materials that can be recycled that are mentioned in the story. Look at this list and put each item into the correct bin. Anything left over should go in a list labelled 'compost heap'.
    potato peelings   kitchen roll tubes   wine bottles   leftovers from lunch
    banana skins   newspapers   old drawing paper   a bent paperclip
    tea-bags   old magazines   rusty nails   a cola can   lager cans   jam jars
    an apple core   old letters   a sauce bottle   a soup tin   a pickle jar

Name ______________________________ Date ______________

Seymour in the Desert

Seymour is an ordinary dragon, except for one thing – he cannot breathe fire and smoke, only rain, wind or snow! Seymour doesn't fit in with his family or friends, so he sets off to find himself a perfect place.

Seymour walked for days on end. The further he walked, the warmer and sunnier the weather became. At last he came to an enormous desert.

"There's certainly enough room here for a dragon," said Seymour. "And it could certainly do with a little rain." Seymour began to cheer up. Perhaps he had found his perfect place at last.

But Seymour did not stay cheered up for long. He soon discovered that dragons weren't very good at walking in sand. It got between their toes and stuck in their scales. There were no shady glens or cosy caves in the desert either.

And the desert wasn't really the place for having a lot of fun. "Life in the desert is hard," said the camels. "There's no time for games and nonsense here."

"That's right," said the sand cats. "Everyone in the desert has to work just to survive. You can't run about and play here."

Seymour thought he might make friends by creating a storm. But when he roared he blew sand across the desert, and the tinier animals with it. "Stop! Stop!" they all shouted together. "You're destroying our homes!"

And when he breathed a storm they shouted even more. "No, no!" they screamed. "We can't have all this rain in the desert. You're mixing everything up!"

Seymour brushed some sand from his scales. "Do you want me to go?" he asked.

Silently, the animals pointed the way across the sand.

From *Seymour Finds a Home* by Dyan Sheldon

Answer these questions in sentences.
Write the answers in your book.

1 What was Seymour looking for?
2 What were the two reasons that made Seymour think he'd found the perfect place?
3 Why did Seymour decide that perhaps the desert wasn't a good place for him? Give three reasons.
4 What happened to the tiny animals when Seymour created the storm?
5 Did the animals become his friends?
6 Why didn't they want rain in the desert?
7 How did Seymour know that the desert animals wanted him to go?
8 Copy this postcard into your book and finish Seymour's message to his Mum and Dad.

Dear Mum and Dad,	Mr. and Mrs. Dragon, 3 Cave Street, Burnham, Dragonshire PUF1 OHO

Name ______________________ Date ______________

Seymour at the North Pole

Seymour is an ordinary dragon, except for one thing – he cannot breathe fire and smoke, only rain, wind or snow! Seymour doesn't fit in with his family or friends, so he sets off to find himself a perfect place.

Seymour walked for days on end. He walked as far from the forest and the farm and the desert as he could get. He walked until he came to a land that was completely frozen and perfectly white. As far as he could see there was absolutely nothing there. It was definitely big enough for a young dragon. He could breathe blizzards here and no one would notice. He could make a storm and no one would care.

"This must be it," Seymour said to himself. "This must be my place."

The other animals were very friendly. "Have a raw fish," offered the polar bears.

But dragons weren't very fond of raw fish. Seymour's nostrils quivered. He made a face. "Yuk," said Seymour. "This smells like old boots."

"Come in for a swim, then," called the seals.

But dragons weren't really suited to swimming in icy pools. Seymour's teeth began to chatter. His scales began to freeze. Icicles dripped from his chin. "I-i-is it always this cold?" stammered Seymour.

The foxes were chasing each other through the snow. "Oh, no," they laughed. "It's often much colder than this."

Never before had Seymour wished that he could breathe fire as much as he wished he could breathe fire now. Even his eyelashes ached from the cold. He snapped an icicle from his chin. "Perhaps this isn't the place for me after all," Seymour sighed.

From *Seymour Finds a Home* by Dyan Sheldon

Read the passage carefully, and then put the following sentences in the correct order to tell the story.

a) The polar bears, foxes and seals were friendly.
b) Seymour thought the fish was revolting.
c) Seymour had walked far from the forest, the farm and the desert.
d) His teeth chattered, his scales froze and icicles dripped from his chin.
e) The polar bears offered him a raw fish.
f) At last Seymour came to a white and frozen land.
g) Seymour nearly froze when he tried to swim in the icy pool with the seals.
h) Seymour decided that perhaps this was not the place for him.
i) He thought the land was big enough for a young dragon to do as he liked.
j) Seymour really wished he could breathe fire when the foxes told him that it sometimes got even colder.

Name ______________________________ Date ______________

The Magical Storyhouse

Simon's Mum was at work, so his big brother Lou was looking after him. Lou was working as a cleaner at a big old house, and he took Simon with him.

Simon looked around and decided that Lou had been pulling his leg. In this house, he was perfectly sure, there were no bones buried under the floorboards in the lounge. The hall was painted white, and hung with pictures, and there was a vase of yellow tulips on a small table beside the telephone. He wasn't even slightly frightened. I'll prove it's not haunted, he thought. I'll go into the lounge and see what's in there.

The room was full of armchairs and sofas covered in velvet, and there was a large mirror on the wall over the mantelpiece. A fat, stripey ginger cat was lying curled up next to a fat, stripey cushion on the windowseat. Simon smiled. "My brother's mad," he said to the cat, who had opened one eye to see what was disturbing his morning snooze. "He says there are bones under the floorboards."

"Not that I know of," said the cat in a furry, purry voice, "although I myself have hunted down a good many moths here, so I daresay there are remains of wings and what have you."

Simon sat down on the nearest armchair. "You can speak," he squeaked.

"Certainly," said the cat. "Most cats can speak. It's simply that there are very few people worth making the effort for."

From *The Magical Storyhouse* by Adèle Geras

Answer these questions in sentences.
Write the answers in your book.

1. Why was Lou looking after Simon?
2. What was Lou's job?
3. List four things Simon found in the hall.
4. What had Lou told Simon about the house?
5. Describe the cat Simon saw in the lounge.
6. What furniture was in the lounge?
7. What had the cat been doing?
8. How do you know Simon was surprised about the talking cat?
9. Why did Simon say Lou was mad?
10. Why, according to the cat, had so few people ever heard a cat speak?

Name ______________________ Date ______________

Zappers!

New Zappers are crackers!

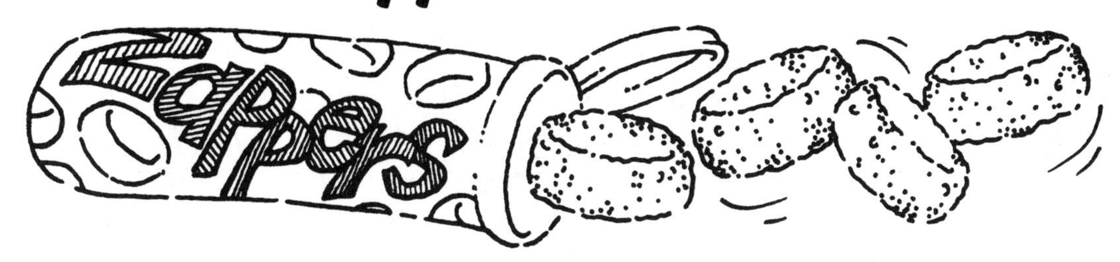

ZAPPERS

SUGAR-COATED CANDY SWEETS IN FOUR DELICIOUS FLAVOURS:

ORANGE LEMON
STRAWBERRY LIME

FIRST THEY'RE CRISPY, THEN THEY'RE CRUNCHY AND MUNCHY!!!

It's the sugar-coated
candy sweet,
A truly delicious
fruity treat!!

Look at the advert and answer these questions in sentences.
Write the answers in your book.

1 What new sweet does this advert want you to buy?
2 Zappers come in which four flavours?
3 List some of the words used to describe Zappers.

4 What is your favourite sweet? Make up your own advert to persuade people to buy it. Make it eye-catching!

Name ______________________ Date ______________

The Terror of the Norsemen

More than 1,000 years ago, the Norsemen from Norway, Sweden and Denmark were great adventurers. They were known as Vikings and their first journeys across the North Sea to Britain were to carry out raids on villages and monasteries in order to steal. They took gold and other treasure, and sometimes slaves. They often set fire to the villages and murdered anyone who tried to stop them. They brought terror to the whole of the country. Their own lands were cold and mountainous, and when they came to Britain they saw good, fertile land. The Vikings decided to settle in Britain in order to farm and trade.

The British did not take kindly to these Viking invaders and many fierce battles were fought. In the north of England, York was captured by the Vikings in 867. They called it Jorvik. In the south of England, King Alfred the Great of Wessex defeated the Vikings but he allowed them to settle in a part of England which became known as Danelaw.

Many Vikings became farmers or craftsmen. They made cloth, metal goods and pots.

The Vikings were the finest shipbuilders in Europe. They built warships called longboats in which they carried out their raids. They were very skilful sailors; their ships had large sails, rudders and many oars. Many of the ships had a large dragon's head on the prow to terrify their enemies.

The Vikings fought with spears, bows and arrows, swords and axes. They wore chain mail and metal helmets to protect themselves and carried large shields.

The Vikings loved to tell stories about their gods and their battles. These stories were called sagas. Many Vikings became Christians.

Archaeologists have found many Viking objects in Britain, and at the Jorvik Museum in York a number of Viking houses and workshops have been rebuilt to show us what life was really like in Viking times.

Read these sentences carefully.
In each sentence there is one word that is not correct.
Write the sentences in your book, leaving out the wrong words and putting in the right ones.

1 The Vikings came from Norway, Sweden and Italy.
2 At first they came to Britain on holiday.
3 They attacked villages and monasteries and stole gold and wood.
4 The Viking lands were cold and flat.
5 The Vikings decided to settle in France.
6 They captured York in the south of England.
7 King Henry the Great defeated the Vikings in the south of England.
8 The Vikings were allowed to live in London.
9 The Viking warships were called ferries.
10 The boats had many oars and large engines.
11 They fought fiercely with spears, swords, axes and guns.
12 They wore chain mail and leather helmets to protect themselves.

Name ______________________ Date ______________

Thor's Hammer

The Vikings were Norsemen from the lands we know today as Norway, Sweden and Denmark. They had many wonderful stories to tell about their gods. These stories were called sagas.

Thor was the son of the most important Norse god Odin. He was known as the god of thunder, and he owned a great hammer.

One day Thor woke up and found that his precious hammer had been stolen. He believed that it had been stolen by the Giants, and that if it was not found, the Giants would take over Asgard which was the home of the gods.

One of the gods, Loki, offered to go and look for the hammer. Disguised as a falcon, he flew to Jotunheim and met Thrym, King of the Giants. Thrym admitted that he had stolen Thor's hammer. He had hidden it deep inside the earth, and would not return it until the goddess Freyja agreed to be his bride.

When Loki returned with this news, Freyja was dreadfully angry; she made the walls shake and the furniture rattle, and she broke her best necklace. She would not go!

The gods and goddesses finally decided on a plan, though Thor was not amused by it. They would dress Thor up in a bridal dress, a veil, brooches and necklaces, and pretend that he was Freyja.

Giant Thrym had made great preparations for his wedding and was delighted to see his "bride". He had no idea that it was Thor in disguise, and was surprised at how hungry his bride was and how fiery her eyes appeared. Loki explained that "she" hadn't eaten or slept much for a week because she was so excited about her wedding to Thrym!

Just as they were about to be married, Thrym had Thor's hammer brought in. Thor grabbed it and Thrym was astonished to see who his "bride" really was. But not for long. Thor was so angry that he used his hammer to destroy all the Giants at the wedding feast. This was to be a lesson to anyone who thought that they could trick the gods.

With reference to *Norse Myths* by Kevin Crossley-Holland

Answer these questions in sentences.
Write the answers in your book.

1. From which lands did the Vikings come?
2. Who was the most important god?
3. What relation was Thor to Odin?
4. What was Thor's most precious possession?
5. What was Asgard?
6. Who went to find the hammer?
7. How was he disguised?
8. Who had stolen the hammer and where was it hidden?
9. What news did Loki bring back to Asgard?
10. What did Freyja do when she heard the news?
11. Who was Thor disguised as when he went to the Giants' kingdom?
12. What was he wearing?
13. How did Loki explain why the "bride" was so hungry and had such fiery eyes?
14. What promise did Thrym keep just before his wedding?
15. What lesson did Thor hope to teach by killing the Giants?

Name ______________________ Date ______________

Dipa (The Lamp)

A song for Diwali

Light the lamp now,
Make bright
the falling light
wrapped in the leaves
of autumn.

Gone is the day,
Kindle the flame
to burn
in the dark,
Let it show
the way.

Lit is the lamp
of the moon,
Brilliant the stars,
Make them shine,
Let them unite,
Let there be light.

By Ann Bonner (from *A Tickle in your Tummy*)

Hinduism is the world's oldest religion. It started in India many centuries ago. One of the special festivals celebrated by Hindus is Diwali, which is often called the Festival of Light. It is celebrated during October and November.

A favourite story for Hindu children is about how, long ago, Prince Rama rescued his wife, Princess Sita, from Ravana the Demon King.

Ravana, the evil Demon King, had ten heads and twenty arms. He believed that if he could marry Princess Sita, he would be ruler of the whole world. He kidnapped Sita and took her from India to the island of Lanka.

Hanuman, King of the Monkeys, found Sita and went back to tell Prince Rama where she was. Rama went to rescue Sita and after a dreadful battle he brought her home.

Hindus celebrate Diwali to remember Rama's return to his kingdom. They light rows of lights or candles in windows and outside their houses to welcome Rama home.

Answer these questions in sentences.
Write the answers in your book.

1 Which words in the poem tell you what season it is?
2 In the poem, why is the flame lit?
3 What does "Let them unite" mean?
4 Who was Ravana?
5 Where had Princess Sita been taken?
6 How did Rama rescue Sita?
7 What does "kindle the flame" mean?
8 What other sources of light are mentioned in the poem?
9 Which Hindu festival is the poem about?
10 What had Ravana done and why?
11 Who found Sita?
12 Why are lamps and candles lit at Diwali?

Name ______________________ Date ______________

Arachne and Athene

Princess Arachne was beautiful and rich, and she was talented too. This led to her becoming boastful.

The greatest of her talents was weaving. She wove beautiful wall hangings and tapestries that were admired by everyone. Unfortunately, Arachne boasted that she was able to weave more skilfully than the goddess Athene herself.

The goddess Athene was not pleased to hear this, so a competition was arranged. She hoped to teach Arachne a lesson.

For days and nights Arachne and Athene worked hard and finally the tapestries were finished. Arachne's tapestry was incredibly beautiful, whilst the goddess Athene's tapestry was good but not as good as Arachne's. Athene was so enraged that she tore Arachne's work to pieces.

Arachne was frightened and upset, and she ran away and hanged herself.

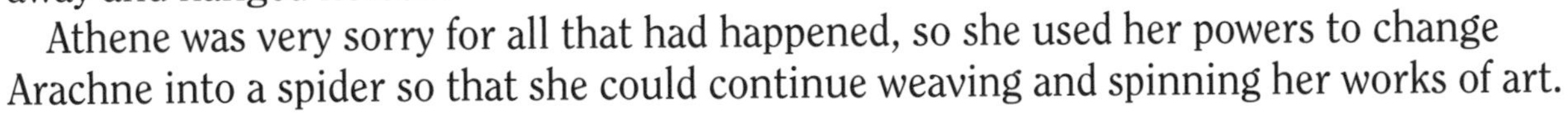

Athene was very sorry for all that had happened, so she used her powers to change Arachne into a spider so that she could continue weaving and spinning her works of art.

Arachne gave her name to the spider family or Arachnids, and you can see her wonderful webs all over the house and garden. The dewy webs in bushes or trees on autumn mornings are especially beautiful.

True, false or "I can't tell"?
Write the answers in your book.

1 Arachne was clever and beautiful.
2 Arachne made beautiful clothes for herself.
3 Athene was very boastful.
4 The competition was to find out who could finish her tapestry first.
5 Arachne was more skilled at weaving than Athene.
6 Athene was angry and jealous of Arachne's skill.
7 Arachne was worried and unhappy.
8 In her anger, Athene changed Arachne into a spider.

In your book, write down one word from the story that means the same as each of these words.

9 clever
10 contest
11 angry
12 at last

Name ______________________ Date ____________

A Martian Comes to Stay

It was on the second day of Peter's holiday with his grandmother that the Martian came to the cottage. There was a knock at the door and when he went to open it there was this small green person with webbed feet and eyes on the end of stumpy antennae who said, perfectly politely, "I wonder if I might bother you for the loan of a spanner?"

"Sure," said Peter. "I'll ask my Gran."

Gran was in the back garden, it being a nice sunny day. Peter said, "There's a Martian at the door who'd like to borrow a spanner."

Gran looked at him over her knitting. "Is there, dear? Have a look in Grandad's toolbox, there should be one in there."

That's not what your grandmother would have said? No, nor mine either, but Peter's Gran was an unusual lady, as you will discover. Grandad had died a few years earlier and she lived alone in this isolated cottage in the country, growing vegetables and keeping chickens, and Peter liked going to stay with her more than almost anything he could think of. She was unflappable and what you might call open-minded, which accounts for everything that happened next.

Peter found the spanner and took it back to the Martian, who held out a rather oddly constructed hand and thanked him warmly. "We've got some trouble with the gears or something and had to make an emergency landing. And now the mechanic says he left his tools back at base. I ask you! It's all a mystery to me – I'm just the steward. Anyhow – thanks a lot. I'll bring it back in a minute." And he padded away up the lane.

There was no one around, but then there wasn't likely to be: the cottage was a quarter of a mile from the village and hardly anyone came by except the occasional farm tractor and the odd holidaymaker who'd got lost.

"Should have offered him a cup of tea," said Gran. "He'll have a fair journey, I shouldn't wonder."

"Yes," said Peter. "I didn't think of that."

In precisely three minutes there was a knock at the door. The Martian was there, looking distinctly agitated. He said, "They've gone."

From *A Martian Comes to Stay* by Penelope Lively

Answer these questions in sentences.
Write the answers in your book.

1. Describe the person who knocked at Gran's door.
2. What did the Martian want?
3. Where was Grandad?
4. List three jobs that kept Gran busy at her cottage.
5. Why had the Martian landed?
6. Why did the Martian need the spanner?
7. What was the Martian's job?
8. Why did Gran say that they should have offered him a cup of tea?
9. Why did the Martian come back?
10. Match each of the words in List **A** to the word or words with the same meaning in list **B**.

A	B
isolated	**from time to time**
unflappable	**made**
occasional	**calm**
agitated	**alone**
distinctly	**disturbed**
emergency	**clearly**
constructed	**a sudden difficulty**

Name ____________________ Date ____________

Hero and Saffo

Hero and his little sister Saffo lived in Athens. Hero was twelve and Saffo was ten.

Life was different for rich and for poor people in Athens. Their parents were quite rich and they had two slaves who helped in the house.

Saffo had lessons every day and could read and write; she was also learning about music and arithmetic. Saffo knew that she would get married when she was about fourteen, for that was the custom. Although Athens was a democracy, women and slaves were not allowed to vote. Huge meetings were held on the Pnyx, and it was the men who decided how the city should be governed; women had very few rights and no power, and poor women had to work hard with no slaves to assist them in running the house.

As he was from a rich family and a boy, Hero spent more time at school than his sister. Poor families could not afford to send their children to school for very long.

Answer these questions in sentences.
Write the answers in your book.

1 Where did Hero and his sister live?

2 What kind of people had slaves?

3 What lessons did Saffo have every day?

4 What was it that slaves and women were not allowed to do?

5 Look in a dictionary to find the meaning of "democracy".

6 Who governed Athens?

7 Why would Hero spend more time at school than many other boys?

Name ______________________ Date ______________

St. David

March 1st is a special day for Welsh people because it is St. David's Day. St. David is the patron saint of Wales. On St. David's Day, churches fly St. David's flag and many Welsh people wear a daffodil to remind them of their patron saint.

David was born in Wales about 1,500 years ago. When he was young, his mother read him stories from the Bible and he became a Christian. As he grew older, he decided to build monasteries in twelve different places in Wales so that holy men called monks could live there and teach the Welsh people about God. Wales was the only country in Britain that had become Christian during Roman times.

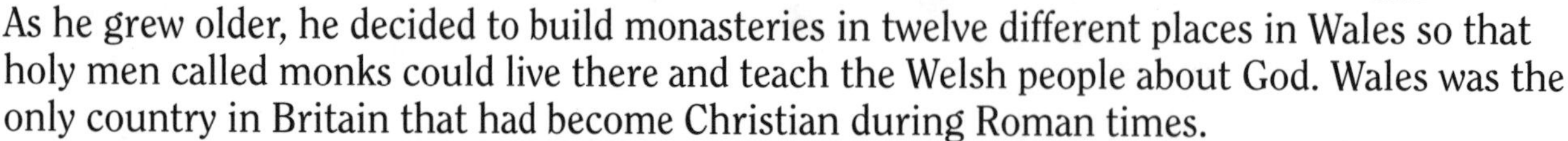

However, one of the places David had chosen was near a robbers' camp. The robbers were very dangerous. They stole and murdered and were feared by everyone. When they saw the monastery being built they were worried. They did not want these good and holy men near them. They wanted to be left alone to continue their life of crime.

At night the robbers did their evil work. Every morning when David and his friends arrived they found stones rolled away, walls pulled down and wood smashed. They were upset by the robbers' wickedness, but it only made them work even harder and faster to finish their building and help the people in the area.

Although it took years of effort, in time the monastery was finished and the monks moved in. They helped all the people in the countryside. They gave lessons to the children, looked after the sick, helped the poor and taught people about God.

The people would no longer put up with the wickedness of the robbers and so it was the robbers who had to go away. David became famous for the many good things that he did and he was made a saint after his death.

Copy these sentences into your book.
Choose a word from the list to fill each space.

1. David was born in ____________ .
2. He wanted to build ____________ in twelve different places.
3. One monastery was near a ____________ camp.
4. The robbers pulled down ____________ and ____________ the wood.
5. The robbers' wickedness only made David work ____________ .
6. When the monastery was finished it was the robbers who had to ____________ .
7. The monks looked after people who were ____________ .
8. They gave ____________ to the children.
9. The monks taught people about ____________ .

monasteries	**God**	**smashed**
harder	**Wales**	**robbers'**
leave	**walls**	**sick**
lessons		

10. Draw a picture of the flower of Wales.

Name ______________________ Date ______________

St. Andrew

Andrew and Peter were brothers. They were fishermen, but they gave up fishing to follow Jesus. As they travelled through the countryside, Jesus taught them about God, and how they should be kind to other people and lead honest lives.

After Jesus was crucified on Good Friday, Andrew and the remaining ten disciples continued to teach the people about God, but the Roman rulers were afraid of their influence and tried to stamp out Christian ideas.

When Andrew was arrested the Roman Governor sentenced him to be put to death on a cross shaped like an X. This was a terrible way to die, but even while he was dying, Andrew still told the crowd of God's goodness.

About 500 years later, Andrew's body was taken from its resting place and put in a special grave with a monk to look after it. One night the monk had a strange dream which he had to obey. He had to take Andrew's body and bury it far away in a special place of God's choosing. After much travelling, the monk reached a quiet, lonely place and there he buried Andrew. That place was in Scotland.

When the people of Scotland became Christian they chose Andrew as their special or patron saint, and they celebrate St. Andrew's Day on November 30th. The cross on the Scottish flag shows the cross on which St. Andrew was put to death.

Answer these questions in sentences.
Write the answers in your book.

1 What relation was Peter to Andrew?
2 Why did they give up being fishermen?
3 Who was trying to stamp out Christianity?
4. How was Andrew put to death?
5 What was different about the cross Andrew died on?
6 Who looked after Andrew's grave?
7 Where was his body taken?
8 When do people celebrate St. Andrew's Day?
9 Draw a picture of the Scottish flag.

Name ______________________________ Date ______________

St. George

St. George probably lived about 200 years after Jesus. He was a soldier in the Roman army. When he became a Christian he left the army because he did not want to put Christians in prison, which was a Roman law.

There are many stories about St. George, but the most famous is about his fight with a dragon.

While travelling through the countryside one day, George came to a city where the people lived in fear of a terrible dragon that lived in a lake just outside the city walls. Whenever the dragon felt hungry he would climb out of the lake and wander the streets of the city, breathing fire and eating anyone he could find. The poor people were terrified and tried to lock themselves in their houses to escape his fiery breath and razor-sharp teeth. For a long time they tried to keep themselves safe by leaving sheep near the lake for the dragon to eat, but soon there were no animals left. The only solution the King could think of was to offer one person as a sacrifice every day to keep the monster well fed and happy.

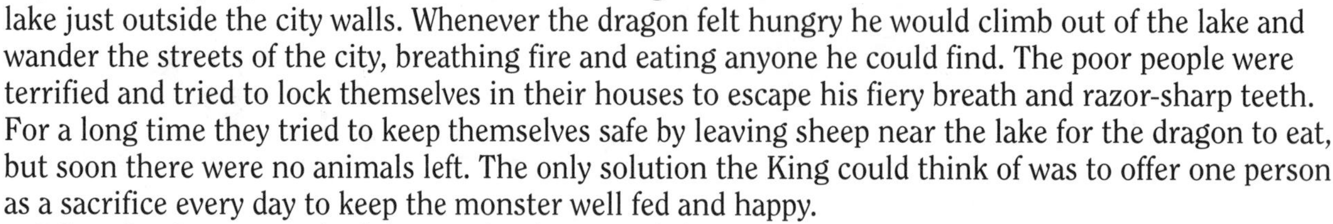

When St. George reached the city, he discovered the King's daughter tied to a post, as she was to be the dragon's next meal. He drew his sword and waited for the dragon to appear. It was a terrible battle, but George knew that if he did not win, the Princess would die too. At last the dragon lay dead and George returned the Princess to her father. He told the King about Jesus and persuaded him and all his people to become Christians.

Though St. George was not English, he was made patron saint of England because he was such a good and brave man. The English decided that he was a good example to follow. St. George's Day is on 23rd April and on this day many people wear the red rose of England. St. George's flag is flown from church flagpoles in his honour.

Use the story of St. George to solve the crossword.

Clues for ACROSS

6 St. George was a __________ man.
7 This saint lived 200 years after Jesus.
8 George told the King about __________ .
11 A word to describe the battle
13 The creature that George fought
16 Where the Romans put the Christians
17 The flower worn on St. George's Day
18 The dragon wandered here.
19 This was George's first job.

Clues for DOWN

1 George did this to the dragon.
2 The people left these animals for the dragon.
3 George became a __________ and left the army.
4 The dragon lived in this.
5 The people __________ themselves in their homes.
9 The dragon had __________ teeth.
10 This person was tied up and left for the dragon.
12 George is the patron saint of this country.
14 A word to describe the dragon's breath
15 St. George's Day is in this month.

Name ______________________ Date ______________

St. Patrick

Patrick was a lucky boy. His parents were rich and he lived a comfortable life in his Welsh homeland.

However, one day when he was sixteen years old, Patrick was captured by some robbers and taken to Ireland to be sold as a slave. He was frightened and homesick, but he had to get used to this new and hard life. His job was to look after sheep, and, whilst sitting among the hills, Patrick used to long for his own home and family.

After some years Patrick grew to like the Irish people and wished he could persuade them to become Christians. At that time the Irish had many gods and believed in magic.

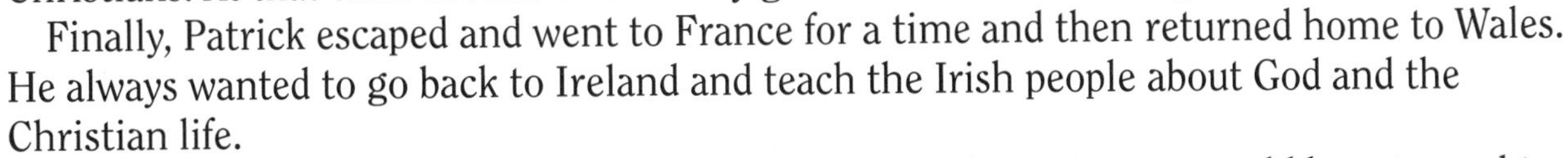

Finally, Patrick escaped and went to France for a time and then returned home to Wales. He always wanted to go back to Ireland and teach the Irish people about God and the Christian life.

He became a priest and then a bishop. When he was about sixty years old he returned to Ireland. He found the King and challenged him to give up the old gods and become a Christian. The King was impressed by Patrick's skilful arguments and eventually became a Christian, much to Patrick's delight.

Patrick spent the rest of his life in Ireland, converting people to Christianity and building churches.

The Irish people now look upon Patrick as their patron saint. St. Patrick's Day is celebrated on 17th March, when many people wear the national plant of Ireland – the shamrock.

Answer these questions in sentences.
Write the answers in your book.

1. Where was St. Patrick born?
2. How old was Patrick when he was captured by the robbers?
3. What was his job as a slave?
4. What did Patrick miss most of all?
5. What did the Irish people believe in?
6. Where did Patrick flee to when he escaped?
7. How old was he when he returned to Ireland?
8. Who was Patrick's first convert?
9. How did Patrick spend the rest of his life?
10. What is the national plant of Ireland?
11. When do we celebrate St. Patrick's Day?
12. Use a dictionary or thesaurus to find a word that means the same as each of these.

impressed **converting** **eventually** **skilful**

Name ______________________ Date ______________

Snakes Alive!

King Polydectes wanted to be rid of a brave young man called Perseus who lived in his palace. After much thought, Polydectes set him the task of killing one of the Gorgon monsters called Medusa and bringing back her head as proof. Medusa was a hideous creature with sharp teeth and snakes writhing around her head.

Perseus was the son of Zeus, the most important of the gods. Perseus was given gifts by the gods to help him complete his task and return safely. He had a strong helmet to protect him and make him invisible, winged sandals to help him fly and a bright, shining shield.

"Take care," said the goddess Athene as she gave him the shield. "You must never look directly at Medusa or you will be turned to stone. Look only at her reflection in this shield to help you destroy her."

Perseus was a brave and confident young man. He flew into the mountains where Medusa lived. Finally, he found her gloomy cavern and crept inside.

At first everything was still, and then, as he advanced, he heard a hissing, shuffling sound as Medusa came towards him, sensing her next victim. Perseus carefully held out his shield and glanced at her reflection in it. He was horrified by the monster he saw there. He forced himself to go towards Medusa, then he struck out at her with his sword. His one powerful blow cut off her head and it rolled across the floor. Keeping his eyes tightly shut, Perseus grasped the monstrous head and put it in his sack. He wasted no time in flying back to King Polydectes.

"Look, I have returned with a gift, Great King!" announced Perseus. King Polydectes was amazed to see Perseus back unharmed. He gazed at the floor where Perseus had unwrapped the gift. That one glance was enough. King Polydectes' heart stopped beating, and he was turned to stone.

True or false?
Write the true sentences in your book.

1. Zeus sent Perseus to kill King Polydectes.
2. King Polydectes sent Perseus to kill Medusa.
3. Medusa was a beautiful goddess.
4. Medusa was a hideous monster.
5. The god Zeus was the father of Perseus.
6. Medusa lived in a fine palace.
7. Athene had snakes writhing around her head.
8. Athene gave Perseus a bright shield.
9. Perseus heard a groaning sound as Medusa came closer.
10. Perseus looked at Medusa's reflection in his shield.

Name ______________________ Date ____________

A Tough Childhood

In the Greek state of Sparta, life was very hard. When a baby was born it had to be perfect. If it was ill or weak it was taken to the mountains and left there to die.

Girls did not go to school but they had to take lots of exercise so that when they grew up they could have strong healthy babies to provide new families of tough Spartans.

Sparta was famous for its large and powerful army. The boys had to be rough and tough if they were to be the next soldiers. From about the age of seven they were sent to boarding schools. These schools were very strict and the boys were whipped frequently. They had to hunt or steal their food. Their beds were hard slabs of stone and they were given only thin clothes to wear, even in the coldest weather. They learned all the fighting skills of the soldier and how to use a sword, shield and spear.

Use the description of Sparta to solve the crossword.

Clues for ACROSS

1 The beds were made of this.
2 The boys were __________ as a punishment.
5 The boys lived in __________ schools.
7 Where the sick babies were left
11 Life was like this in Sparta.
13 A soldier uses a __________ for protection.
14 Opposite of hard
15 What new babies had to be
16 The people lived in __________ .

Clues for DOWN

1 The age the boys started school
3 The girls took lots of this.
4 A short weapon
6 It is wrong to __________ someone's things.
8 The boys were trained to be these.
9 The schools were very __________ .
10 Where the girls stayed
12 Sparta was famous for its __________ .
13 A throwing weapon

Name ______________________ Date ______________

The Martian Goes to the Fête

The day of the fête was fine and dry. The Martian was installed in the pushchair, swathed in a blue rug that Gran had crocheted a long time ago and with an old pixie hood that had belonged to Peter's sister on his head. His antennae poked out through two holes, which did not look quite right, so they had to fix a sunshade to the handles of the pushchair and drape some muslin over it; in this the Martian was only dimly visible as a muffled form.

"We'll say he's sensitive to sunstroke," said Gran, "if anyone gets nosy."

They set off for the village with Peter in charge of the pushchair.

The Martian was fascinated with everything he saw. He asked them to stop for him to admire the Amoco Garage with its swags of flapping plastic flags and brightly coloured signs about "Four-Star Petrol" and "Credit Cards Accepted". He found it, he declared, very beautiful.

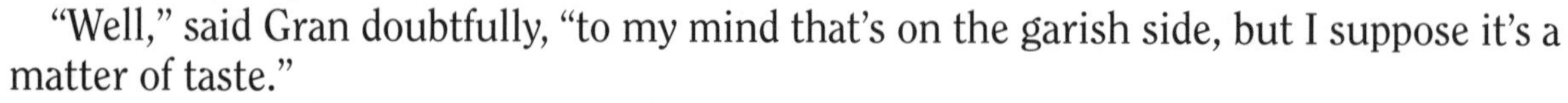

"Well," said Gran doubtfully, "to my mind that's on the garish side, but I suppose it's a matter of taste."

The Martian said humbly that he probably hadn't been here long enough yet to be much of a judge of these things. He gazed at the display of baked bean tins and cornflake packets in the window of the Minimarket and asked anxiously if that would be considered handsome.

"Not really," said Peter. "I mean, it's the sort of thing that's so ordinary you don't really notice."

"He's seeing a different angle," said Gran. "Stands to reason, when you think about it."

From *A Martian Comes to Stay* by Penelope Lively

Answer these questions in sentences.
Write the answers in your book.

1 Where were Gran and Peter taking the Martian?
2 Why do you think they wrapped the Martian up so carefully?
3 Which things did the Martian greatly admire on his way to the fête?
4 Did Gran agree with him?
5 What did he see in the Minimarket?
6 Why didn't Peter admire the display?

Write down one word from the story that means the same as each of these words.

7 placed	**14 enthralled**
8 wrapped	**15 taken**
9 hang	**16 said**
10 vaguely	**17 uncertainly**
11 seen	**18 bright**
12 inquisitive	**19 uneasily**
13 stared	**20 viewpoint**

Name ______________________ Date ______________

Ben's Big Day

Ben wasn't going to like his new school. He knew that now, as sure as eggs is eggs.

"How can you be so sure?" his Mum called from the kitchen.

"Just am!" said Ben.

He flicked over channels on the telly: they were all boring.

"That Miss Kirby is horrible," he said. "She never smiles."

"Who says she never smiles?"

"Everybody. She makes you stand against walls."

"Who's everybody?"

"The boy from the papershop," said Ben.

"The boy from the papershop doesn't know everything," his Mum said.

Ben noticed she didn't mention what the girl from upstairs had told her. She'd told his Mum about a big, rough boy at school whose name was Bernie Flowers. But his Mum didn't mention that, of course.

She said, "You'll make a lot of new friends, just wait and see."

"I don't want new friends," he said.

"What do you want, Ben Adams?" his Mum asked.

"I told you."

"No pets, Ben! We've already discussed that," she said.

He wasn't asking for anything fancy. Not a whole tribe of baboons. Not even one. Just a cat would do. If he had a cat he'd call it Bonzo.

"Fine name for a cat!" his Dad always said.

Mrs. Shastri, who lived on the ground floor of their house, had a cat called Santi. Whenever he came up to see them Ben's Dad said, "Watch out, here comes Santi Claws!" because he dug his claws in really hard and sometimes bit you. But Ben didn't mind. When they were in their other house Ben had almost talked his Mum into having a cat. But just round the corner from Cable Street – where they lived now – there was a busy road.

"No place at all to bring a cat up," his Mum kept saying. "Besides, who'll be at home to look after it?"

From *Ben's Big Day* by Dick Cate

Answer these questions in sentences.
Write the answers in your book.

1 Why was Ben unhappy?
2 What had the girl upstairs told Mum about the school?
3 Why didn't Mum tell Ben about what the girl upstairs had told her?
4 What did Ben want more than anything else?
5 What was the name of Santi's owner?
6 What nickname did Dad give Mrs. Shastri's cat?
7 Why did Dad give the cat that nickname?
8 Why didn't Mum think they should get a cat now?
9 List three different jobs you have to do if you are looking after a cat.

Name ______________________________ Date ______________

The Dinosaur Robbers

Tyrannosaurus Rex and Triceratops may look real, but they're actually two robotic dinosaurs invented by Max's Dad. However, Buster's and Binbag's beady eyes spot the dinosaurs and decide they'll come in handy for a bit of burglary.

Binbag had the sneakiest eyes in the street. He and his wife Buster lived just round the corner from Max. Buster and Binbag were robbers. Nobody knew they were robbers of course, because they were very cunning. Buster had arms like a JCB, with lots of tattoos down them. She got her name from busting into houses.

Binbag was very thin and scrawny. After his wife had smashed into a house he would nip inside and stuff all the valuables into black binbags, and that was how he got his name.

Binbag leaned out of his bedroom window. He was staring at the dancing dinosaurs in Max's back garden.

"Whoopee!" he cried. "See those robot dinosaurs? Guess what? We're going to steal one!"

"What do you want a robot dinosaur for?" demanded Buster. "You big baby!"

"We shall use it to break into the jewellery store in the High Street," said Binbag.

"Brilliant idea!" shouted Buster. "Have a smackeroo!" And she gave her husband a big, wet kiss.

That same night the robbers crept into Max's garden. Buster sat on top of Triceratops and Binbag climbed inside. He pushed the STOP – START button and grabbed the levers. Triceratops lurched into action and they went galloping off down the road.

From *The Dinosaur Robbers* by Jeremy Strong

Answer these questions in sentences.
Write the answers in your book.

1. What are Tyrannosaurus Rex and Triceratops?
2. Who made them?
3. What did Buster and Binbag do for a living?
4. How had Buster got her name?
5. How had Binbag got his name?
6. What great idea did Binbag think of?
7. What sort of things would they be able to steal?
8. Which robotic dinosaur did they steal?
9. What did Binbag do to start the robot?
10. At what speed did they travel?
11. These words describe Buster and Binbag. Write their names in your book and put the correct words under each.

dishonest	**thin**	**tattooed**
strong	**scrawny**	**cunning**
sneaky	**quick**	**athletic**
enthusiastic	**powerful**	**well-built**

12. Draw a picture of Buster and Binbag galloping down the road with Triceratops. Keep to the description in the story.

Name ______________________ Date ______________

The Great Wall of China

The Great Wall of China was built more than 2,000 years ago to keep out China's enemies. It is still there today. It is wider and taller than a house. It winds, like a giant snake, for hundreds of kilometres, over mountains and hills. The Emperor, who ordered the wall to be built, was very cruel. He made thousands of men leave their homes and families and go north to build the wall for him. Not many returned home. Most of the men died building the wall.

A story about a lady called Meng Jiang-nu tells us how much people suffered while building the Great Wall.

Meng Jiang-nu lived happily in a village with her husband. One day her husband, who was a builder, was taken away by the Emperor's soldiers. He was forced to work on the Great Wall for many years.

When her husband did not return home, Meng set off to find him. She reached the Great Wall and saw groups of tired, thin men building the wall and soldiers whipping those who rested. An old man told her that her husband had died. She searched for his body, and the gods took pity on her and showed her where he lay. Meng wept for her husband.

The cruel Emperor came to inspect the wall. The Emperor wanted to make Meng one of his wives and promised to place Meng's husband in a wonderful tomb if Meng would marry him.

As soon as her husband had been placed in his tomb, Meng looked with hatred at the Emperor and threw herself into a nearby river. As she drowned, the gods changed her into a beautiful silver fish.

Answer these questions in sentences.
Write the answers in your book.

1 How long has the Great Wall been standing?
2 Why was it built?
3 In which part of China is the Great Wall?
4 Who ordered it to be built?
5 Who built it?
6 What was the high price of building the wall?
7 Why did the soldiers take Meng's husband?
8 Give three reasons for thinking that the builders were badly treated.
9 Why did Meng cry?
10 Why did Meng agree to marry the Emperor?
11 Why did Meng hate the Emperor?
12 What happened to Meng in the end?

Name ______________________ Date ______________

The Queen Cat

In Ancient Egypt, cats were sacred. The Queen Cat lived in the Temple of Bastet in the city of Bubastis. One day, two sisters, Zaita and Tiya, came from the temple to tell their little sister Mew-Sheri some sad news.

"The Queen Cat is dead," said Zaita.

All Mew-Sheri's life the Queen Cat had lived in the Temple of Bastet, the temple of the Cat Goddess, in the heart of the city of Bubastis.

"Will there be a new Queen Cat?" she asked.

"Yes," said Tiya. "But she will not be one of the temple cats; she will come from outside."

"Who will choose her?"

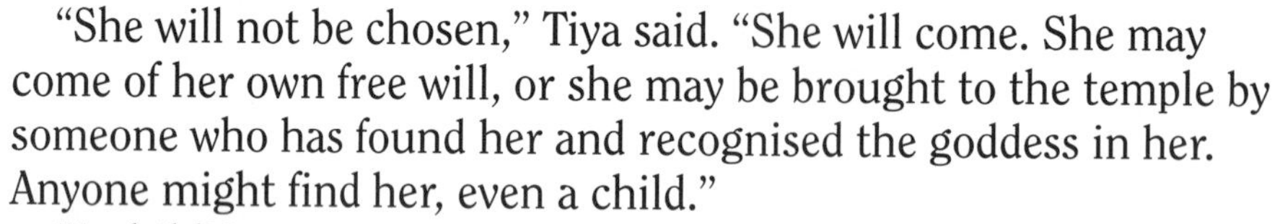

"She will not be chosen," Tiya said. "She will come. She may come of her own free will, or she may be brought to the temple by someone who has found her and recognised the goddess in her. Anyone might find her, even a child."

"A child?"

Tiya smiled. "Yes. Perhaps even you, Pussycat."

"How would I know her – if I found her?" asked Mew-Sheri. "What colour will she be? Will she be big? Will she be beautiful?"

"She won't be any particular colour, or size, and she may not even be beautiful," said Tiya. "But she will be special, and if you found her – you would simply know. You would know that she was the one."

Mew-Sheri was staring at her sister with big eyes. "I'm going to find her," she said.

Zaita was scornful. "Don't be silly. There are thousands of cats in Egypt. She might be any cat, from here in the Delta right down to Nubia."

"But wherever she is now," said Mew-Sheri, "she will come to Bubastis, because she is the goddess. And I shall find her."

From *The Queen Cat* by Ann Turnbull

1 In which country does this story take place?
2 What was the sad news which Zaita and Tiya brought to Mew-Sheri?
3 Where in the city did the Queen Cat live?
4 How were the people going to find a new Queen Cat?
5 What would the new Queen Cat be like?
6 Who decided to try to find the new Queen Cat?
7 What were the names of Mew-Sheri's two sisters?
8 Did they think Mew-Sheri would find the Queen Cat?
9 Where would Mew-Sheri have to search for the Queen Cat?

Use a dictionary to find out what these words mean.

10 sacred
11 scornful
12 delta

Name ______________________ Date ______________

Lost and Found

Luxor, Egypt, November 1922

Musah was twelve years old; he was hot, thirsty and exhausted. He had been working since sunrise and now, seven hours later, he was relieved as the midday break came and he could rest in the shade.

He knew he was lucky to have this work because it helped to bring in extra money for his family who were desperately poor. But the work was back-breaking: digging and shifting piles of rocks and sand on the orders of an Englishman who was convinced that an ancient tomb was close by.

For years this Englishman, Howard Carter, had dreamed of finding the tomb of one of the Pharaohs – Tutankhamun. He had been lucky to find a wealthy man who shared his interest. This man was Lord Carnarvon, who agreed to pay for the expedition. But after many seasons of searching the area, the team of archaeologists and labourers had found nothing and Howard Carter was facing the failure of his dream. Lord Carnarvon was becoming impatient and wanted to abandon the expedition.

Their break over, the labourers went back to work, but as he hurried to rejoin his workmates, Musah stubbed his foot on a sharp block of rock. He sat down, clutching his grazed toes. As he did so, he realised that the block was regular in size and shape, not an odd boulder. He called the foreman who excitedly approached Howard Carter to ask him to come and look.

They scraped away the sand and rocks to reveal a flight of sixteen steps which seemed to go down into the heart of the hillside.

Musah had actually stumbled on the steps to a tomb that had been undisturbed for thousands of years – the tomb of Tutankhamun!

Answer these questions in sentences.
Write the answers in your book.

1. Give two reasons why Musah was glad of a rest.
2. Why did Musah think he was lucky?
3. What were the workmen searching for?
4. Who was in charge of the expedition?
5. Who was paying for the search?
6. What is the name given to people who study history and dig for historical items?
7. What is the name given to the workmen who did the heavy digging?
8. Why was Howard Carter losing hope?
9. How did Musah find the stone block?
10. What was the stone block?
11. What did his find lead to?

Use a dictionary to find out what these words mean.

12 abandon
13 stubbed
14 approached
15 undisturbed

Name ______________________________ Date ______________

Sir Garibald and Hot Nose

Sir Garibald had a pet dragon called Hot Nose who was tame and friendly. The people from a village called Greenways asked Sir Garibald to help them by fighting a dragon who had come to their village and was frightening them.

"Just along there!" they said. And they hid. Trembling, Sir Garibald got off his motorbike and crept into the marketplace. Hot Nose could hardly bear to watch. The second dragon was stamping its feet and breathing out fire.

In a high, trembling voice Sir Garibald called, "D...D...D...Dragon! G...Go away! Or I'll f...f...f...fight you!"

The dragon stood still and looked at him. "Fight me! What for?"

"For f...f...frightening people," said Sir Garibald. "S...s...stamping your feet, and b...b...breathing out fire."

"How misunderstood can a dragon be?" glared the dragon. "Never judge a person till you know them! I'm not trying to frighten people. I'm cold. I'm trying to keep warm!"

Sir Garibald looked doubtfully at the dragon. Was it telling the truth?

"In any case, I never eat people," added the dragon. "I'm a vegetarian. But I do feel cold." It blew out more fire, trying to warm its feet.

Sir Garibald was sorry for it. He thought hard. Then he said, "Wait!"

He unwound the long woolly scarf he always wore when he rode his motorbike. Quickly he wound it round the dragon's neck. Then he sat down and took off his shoes. He pulled off the warm stretchy socks he always wore when he rode his motorbike. He fitted his socks on to the dragon's back feet. Next, he reached into his pockets and pulled out the warm stretchy gloves he always had with him when he rode his motorbike. He tugged them on to the dragon's front feet.

"How's that?" he asked.

"Much better!" smiled the dragon. "Thank you. I can fly on now. I'm a long way from home, you know."

Sir Garibald stepped back. The dragon flapped its wings, rose into the air and flew off.

The villagers saw it go. They came running up. "Well done!" they cried.

From *Sir Garibald and Hot Nose* by Marjorie Newman

Answer these questions in sentences.
Write the answers in your book.

1. Why did the villagers of Greenways hide?
2. What clue is there at the beginning of the story that Sir Garibald was not an ordinary knight?
3. Why didn't Hot Nose want to watch?
4. How can you tell from the story that Sir Garibald was frightened of the dragon?
5. How did the dragon frighten people?
6. How did the dragon feel when Sir Garibald said he was going to fight it because it was frightening people?
7. What was the dragon trying to do?
8. What did the dragon say that made Sir Garibald believe it was harmless?
9. How did Sir Garibald feel?
10. What did Sir Garibald do to help the dragon?
11. Why did Sir Garibald always wear such warm woolly clothing?
12. Why does this story have a happy ending?

Name ________________________ Date ______________

Guy Fawkes and the Gunpowder Gang

On the night of the fifth of November, the people of London had celebrated the failure of the Gunpowder Plot. They lit bonfires and threw straw figures of Guy Fawkes into the flames to see him burn. Now, on the last day of January, 1606, the crowd were screaming for his blood.

Guy Fawkes stared up at the waiting hangman. He shivered, but not with fear. The cold January wind cut through his thin clothes. He caught the eye of his close friend, Thomas Winter.

"Be brave, Tom!" he cried over the noise of the crowd.

"Farewell!" came the reply. "Till we meet again in a better place."

The guard told them to be silent. "It will be Hell, not Heaven, where traitors like you are going this day," he sneered.

Guy turned pale. He was being saved until last, but he could not bear to watch. He looked away towards the House of Lords, the very building they had hoped to destroy. It was too late for any more hopes and dreams. This was the end.

Guy heard Tom mounting the hangman's scaffold and wondered if he was thinking about his elder brother. Robert Winter had been among the first group of four plotters executed the day before.

"I die a true Catholic," Tom cried out to the jeering crowd. Jeers turned to cheers as he swung on the rope and was then carried off to the axeman's block. And the excitement grew as the next two men met the same fate. Here came the moment they had all been waiting for. After his torture, Guy needed help to climb the steps of the ladder up to the scaffold. Once there, he knelt in full view of the crowd and made the sign of the cross. "I ask the King and God for forgiveness," he prayed aloud. "I am not afraid to die."

The life of Guy Fawkes was over – but his fame would live on for ever and ever!

From *Guy Fawkes and the Gunpowder Gang* by Rob Childs

Answer these questions in sentences.
Write the answers in your book.

1. The crowd burned figures of Guy Fawkes. From what were the figures made?
2. What was the date of Guy Fawkes' execution?
3. Why did Guy Fawkes shiver as he saw the hangman?
4. What was the name of Thomas Winter's brother?
5. What happened to Thomas Winter's brother?
6. Which building had the plotters tried to destroy?
7. In this story, how many plotters altogether had been sentenced to death?
8. Why did Guy Fawkes need help to climb the ladder to the scaffold?
9. What were Guy Fawkes last words?
10. How do we remember Guy Fawkes and his plot each year?

Name ______________________________ Date ______________

Two Left Feet

My uncle is a neat little man, with silverish hair, a fine brow, a big nose, a tremendous voice; and, says my father, **two left feet**. There, and even my mother has to admit it, my father **has a point**. My uncle had never been a great success in life. **The truth of the matter is**, he is more of a thinker than a doer; he likes to sit by the fire, just thinking. My father says he is a lazy, no-good layabout, and if he wasn't my mother's brother, he'd be out of our cave **faster than smoke**.

Usually my uncle, who is the best-tempered man in the world, takes my father's remarks in good part. He smiles and nods as if he agrees with every word of them; but the other day – it was five days ago – my father said something that **got under my uncle's skin**. You could tell by the way he looked up, as if he'd sat on a sharp stone. "If only," my father said to my mother, "he **got his hands dirty** once in a while, I'd have a little more respect for him."

Next morning, after my father had gone hunting, my uncle said he was going out.

"Where to?" asked my mother; but he only smiled and **tapped the side of his nose**.

He was gone for about two hours. When he came back, his eyes were shining hugely. He'd found just the thing, he said, that would please my father enormously. He wanted me and my sisters to help him fetch it back.

It turned out to be a hollow treetrunk, as smooth and pale as stone. It was exactly the right size and height, he explained, for my father to stand his spears in.

We brought it back and stood it upright at the entrance to our cave. My mother thought it looked very well; but wouldn't it be better if my uncle cut off the branch that was sticking out from the bottom?

No, said my uncle wisely, it was needed to keep the trunk steady.

My father came home quite late. He'd killed a pig and was carrying it over his shoulder. "Dinner for nine!" he called out cheerfully; then he tripped over the branch and broke his toe.

We finished off the pig that night, which was five days ago; and as my father prophesied, it was the last good meal we've had.

Every morning my uncle sets off into the forest, and every afternoon he comes back, worse than **empty-handed**. Already he's lost my father's best spear and the head off my mother's axe. This morning, he took my father's club.

"It's his last chance!" shouted my father, loudly enough for my uncle to hear.

"If he doesn't come back with something for the pot, I'll put him in it, so help me, I will!"

From *Sabre-tooth Sandwich* by Leon Garfield

---

1 In the passage eight groups of words are in bold print. Write each of these groups of words in your book. Then choose a word or group of words which means the same thing from the list below.

with nothing → empty-handed
annoyed my uncle
a habit of doing the wrong thing
did some real work
told her to mind her own business
the fact is
very quickly
is right

Answer these questions in sentences.
Write the answers in your book.

2 How many people were in the family altogether?
3 "His eyes were shining hugely." What does this tell you about how Uncle was feeling?
4 Why did Uncle bring Father a present?
5 What went wrong with the present?
6 What has Uncle done that is even worse than not catching any food for the family?
7 What has Father threatened to do to Uncle if he returns again with nothing?

Name ______________________ Date ______________

The Excitement of being Ernest

Ernest was a handsome dog with a honey-coloured coat, short droopy ears and a fine beard and moustaches. Ernest had a problem: he didn't know exactly what breed of dog he was. He asked all the dogs in his village, but with no success. One day he met a new dog in the village...

"Hello," he said. "I haven't seen you here before."

"We've only just moved in," said the friendly stranger. "You're the first dog I've met here, actually. Are there a lot in the village?"

"Yes."

"Decent bunch?"

Ernest considered how best to answer this.

"They're all very well bred," he said. "I imagine they've got pedigrees as long as your tail," he added, "as you have, I suppose?"

"You could say that," replied the other. "For what it's worth."

Ernest sighed. I'll give it one more go, he thought. "Straight question," he said. "What sort of dog are you?"

"Straight answer. English Setter."

"English?" said Ernest delightedly. "Well, that makes a change."

"How do you mean?"

"Why, the rest of them are a pack of foreigners. Chinese, German, Tibetan, Irish, American, Finnish – there's no end to the list."

"Really? No, no, I'm as English as you are."

"Ah," said Ernest carefully. "Then you know what sort of dog I am?"

"Of course," said the English Setter. "You're a Gloucestershire Cow Dog."

The hair over Ernest's face prevented the Setter from seeing the changing expression that flitted across it, first of astonishment, then of excitement, and finally a studied look of smug satisfaction.

"Ah," said Ernest. "You knew. Not many people do."

"My dear chap," said the Setter. "You amaze me. I should have thought that any dog would have recognised a Gloucestershire Cow Dog immediately."

"Really?" said Ernest. "Well, I suppose any English dog would."

From *The Excitement of being Ernest* by Dick King-Smith

Answer these questions in sentences.
Write the answers in your book.

1 Why hadn't Ernest seen the stranger before?
2 What breed of dog was the stranger?
3 What breed of dog did the stranger say Ernest was?
4 Why couldn't the stranger see the expression on Ernest's face?
5 How did Ernest feel? Write down the words that tell you this.
6 Why did Ernest think the other dogs didn't know his breed?
7 Match each of these words from the story (list **A**) to a word on the same line in list **B**.

A	B		
decent	**strange**	**normal**	**respectable**
considered	**decided**	**thought**	**knew**
prevented	**helped**	**interrupted**	**stopped**
expression	**thought**	**look**	**grin**
satisfaction	**pleasure**	**anxiety**	**hope**
recognised	**seen**	**known**	**greeted**

Name ______________________ Date ______________

Changing Times

Although not all children would agree, children today are very lucky to be able to attend school between the ages of five and sixteen. These are years in which they can be free to grow, learn and enjoy themselves.

Just over 150 years ago, things were very different. After Victoria became Queen of England, Britain changed a great deal. The population increased very quickly, particularly in the towns. A great number of machines were invented. Though some people led comfortable lives, many were very poor. Until 1870, when it became law for all children aged between five and ten to attend school, many children received no education at all and had to work long hours in factories, down mines, on farms or as street traders. The work was very hard. The children often worked twelve hours a day and were paid just a few pence a week. They often worked in dangerous conditions and there were many accidents. The children were poorly fed and often ill treated.

Even after 1870, some children did not go to school because their parents could not afford the few pence they had to pay for schooling, and they needed their children to work in order to earn money. The factory owners wanted children to work because they could pay low wages to children.

It was only in 1891 that schooling became free to all children; even then, some parents broke the law by sending their children out to work instead. Childhood was not the happy time that most children enjoy today.

True or false?
In your book, copy out the sentences which are true.

1. Children today start school when they are six years old.
2. Children today must stay at school until they are sixteen.
3. In 1870 the law was that children aged between five and sixteen went to school.
4. Many parents needed the wages the children brought home.
5. Until 1870 many children worked long hours at home and in offices.
6. In Victorian times children were paid very low wages for working.
7. Some children worked in mines and factories.
8. After 1891 everyone obeyed the law and sent their children to school.

Answer these questions in sentences.
Write the answers in your book.

9. Describe two ways in which England changed while Victoria was Queen.
10. Name three jobs that were done by children in early Victorian times.
11. Why did factory owners want children to work for them?
12. After 1891, why did some parents still break the law and send their children out to work?
13. List three ways in which you think your life is better than that of children in Victorian times.

Name ______________________ Date ______________

A Faulty Toy

36, Bollom Avenue
Denford
Leeside
LS4 7XP
Monday 29th May.

The Manager,
Bardale Toys
High Street
Bardale
Leeside
LS5 9PG

Dear Sir/Madam,

Last Saturday I made a special trip into town with my Dad to buy a Super-Ray Mark III remote controlled car. I have been saving my pocket money for months and was really looking forward to getting it. I bought it from your shop and went straight home to try it out. After all those months of waiting you can imagine how upset I was when it didn't work. Although it already had new batteries, my Dad put some other new ones in to see if the batteries were faulty, but it still won't go.

I am really disappointed, and Dad is cross because we made a special journey into town just to buy that one thing.

We are sending it back and would like you to send another one to us. It must be exactly the same model. If you can't do this I'd like a refund please.

Yours faithfully

Chris Baker

Answer these questions in sentences.
Write the answers in your book.

1. What did Chris buy on Saturday?
2. Why is Chris writing this letter?
3. To whom is he writing?
4. Why is Dad so cross?
5. How did Chris get the money to buy the car?
6. Why was Chris so disappointed when the car didn't work?
7. On which date did they go to buy the car?
8. What does Chris want the toyshop manager to do?
9. How did Dad check to make sure that it was the car that was faulty?
10. Pretend you are the toyshop manager. Write a letter back to Chris; you must decide whether you are going to send him a new car or refund his money.

Name ______________________ Date ____________

Androcles and the Lion

A long time ago in Ancient Rome there was a poor slave called Androcles. His master was very cruel. Each night, Androcles would lie on his hard bed and dream of escaping, but he knew that if he was caught the punishment would be death.

Androcles' master was making a trip to Africa to buy oil, herbs and spices, and he took Androcles with him. They travelled on a large cargo ship with some animal catchers who were going to bring back wild animals to sell in Rome.

Africa seemed a very strange place to Androcles. There were different languages and different foods, and it was all such a long way from Rome. If he escaped here, perhaps they would never find him.

Very late one night he crept silently out of the camp, keeping low and sneaking from tree to tree. As soon as he was past the sentry he began to run. There were no roads or even paths to follow. He just ran blindly through the jungle until he flopped, exhausted, on the ground. He heard a noise behind him and there, watching him, was the most enormous lion.

The lion gave a roar, and then another. Androcles was too terrified to move. The lion came towards him, but it was limping and Androcles saw that one paw was covered in blood. He felt sorry for the poor animal and slowly he reached out and gently touched the injured paw. A long, sharp thorn was stuck in the soft pad. Very carefully he eased the thorn out, and the lion gave a huge roar of pain as it came free. Androcles shrank back, sure he was about to be eaten, but the lion just curled up at his feet. When Androcles walked away the lion followed him, and the two became friends.

For the next three years, Androcles and the lion lived in a cave. Each day, the lion would go hunting to catch food. Although Androcles had his freedom, he was lonely and he made up his mind to return to Rome. He was sure that no one would recognise him now.

However, one of the first people he saw was his old master who immediately had him arrested. For his punishment he was sentenced to be fed to the lions. The terrible day came and Androcles was led into the arena. The crowd were yelling and shouting. Androcles saw the cage begin to open, and hid his face.

The noise from the crowd suddenly stopped. Androcles peeped through his fingers. There was the lion – his lion – sitting quietly in front of him. The crowd had never seen anything like this before, and they went wild. Androcles was finally granted his freedom.

Answer these questions in sentences.
Write the answers in your book.

1 Who was Androcles running away from?
2 Why was he being chased?
3 What punishment awaited him?
4 Which sentence describes how he felt when he first saw the lion?
5 Why do you think the lion did not attack him in the arena?
6 What was wrong with the lion's paw?
7 Where were the prisoners taken to be killed?
8 The letters of these words have been jumbled up. Write down the correct words. All the words can be found in the story.

hornt	**easerrtd**	**inlo**
scrndAelo	**refomed**	**nreaa**

Name ________________________ Date ____________

Latch Key

My best friend Danny comes to dinner with a key
round his neck, tied on with a piece of string.
At night when no one's home he lets himself in,
even though he is only seven, only seven.
My mum says he's too young and it's a shame.
He watches TV alone and eats crisps left for him.
And Mrs. Robinson – the old woman next door -
listens out for him. Though my Mum says
she is hard of hearing. What does that mean?
Danny's Mummy is always rushing off somewhere,
all dressed up to the nines, and sometimes
when the taxi comes she throws a kiss
like a piece of bread to a duck; it drops on our street
with a sigh. Then Danny scoops up his kiss
and comes into our house holding on to it.
"Can Danny have a bath with me?" I plead,
and my Mum sighs yes, she supposes so,
because he is only seven, only seven.

By Jackie Kay (from *A Tickle in your Tummy*)

Answer these questions in sentences.
Write the answers in your book.

1. Why does Danny have a key?
2. Why do you think that the key is on a piece of string round his neck?
3. What does the poet's Mum think about Danny?
4. What does Danny do on his own?
5. What does "hard of hearing" mean?
6. Why does Danny's Mum leave him alone in the house?
7. What transport does Danny's Mum use?
8. Why do you think Danny scoops up the kiss that his Mum throws to him?
9. Why do you think the poet repeats "only seven, only seven"?
10. Give another word for "plead". Don't forget to use a dictionary.

Name ______________________ Date ______________

The Valley of the Ants

This story comes from the Muslim holy book, the Koran. It is one of the many stories that show how Allah is ***merciful****, even to the smallest of his creatures.*

The queen ant thought quickly. She **summoned** the ants together and told them to gather up as much food as they could and to stay close to their nests. And she told them not to panic. Then the queen climbed to the top of the tallest nest and **peered** down the **valley** in the direction of the terrible noise. A great grey shape was coming closer and closer. At last, the queen could make out what it was – a huge and **magnificent** army of soldiers on foot and on horseback, led by the great prophet, Sulaiman (Solomon). The noise the ants could hear was the stomp, stomp, stomp of the army's marching feet. There was no time to lose.

"The prophet Sulaiman and his army are coming into our valley," the queen told the ants. "That is the noise you can hear. Now go to your nests, as quickly as you can, to **avoid** being crushed. We are so small, the soldiers might not see us in time."

But Sulaiman heard the queen's words and he understood them, for Allah had taught his **prophet** the language of the birds and of all the other animals. He smiled gently and ordered his **mighty** army to stop marching. The terrible noise stopped with them. Sulaiman **instructed** his soldiers to tread very carefully as they moved through the valley so that they would not step on any of the ants. And, truth to tell, so light were their steps, that not a single ant was killed.

From *Out of the Ark* by Anita Ganieri

Answer these questions in sentences.
Write the answers in your book.

1 From which book does this story come?
2 This is the holy book of which religion?
3 What does the story show about Allah?
4 Which three orders did the queen give to the ants?
5 What was causing the ants so much concern?
6 Where did the queen go to get the best view?
7 What was the huge grey shape?
8 What was causing the noise?
9 How could Sulaiman understand what the queen ant said?
10 What order did Sulaiman give his army?
11 What was the result of this order?
12 There are nine words in bold type in the story.
Look each one up in a dictionary and write down its meaning.

Name ______________________ Date ____________

Gilbert

I hope that he'll not come again,
that nasty Mister Hurricane.

You see, that man is not polite;
he sends farm animals into flight,
and every time that man did sneeze,
he bent back zinc and ripped up trees.
He took his claws and scratched the land,
cleaned his nails and sprinkled sand.

I hope that he'll not come again,
that nasty Mister Hurricane.

He ate us out of house and home,
disconnected light and phone,
and when he'd had enough of fun,
left as quickly as he'd come.

I hope that he'll not come again,
that nasty Mister Hurricane.

By Pauline Stewart (from *A Tickle in your Tummy*)

Answer these questions in sentences.
Write the answers in your book.

1 Hurricanes are always given names. What was the name of this hurricane?
2 What effect did the hurricane have on the farm animals?
3 The hurricane bent and tore the roofs. What were they made of?
4 How does the poet describe each gust of wind?
5 What happened after the hurricane had dragged plants and soil from the ground?
6 What do you think "He ate us out of house and home" means?
7 What did the hurricane do to the phone and the light?
8 Why do you think the poet repeats the lines:
"I hope that he'll not come again,
That nasty Mister Hurricane."

Name ______________________ Date ______________

Caesar's Ransom

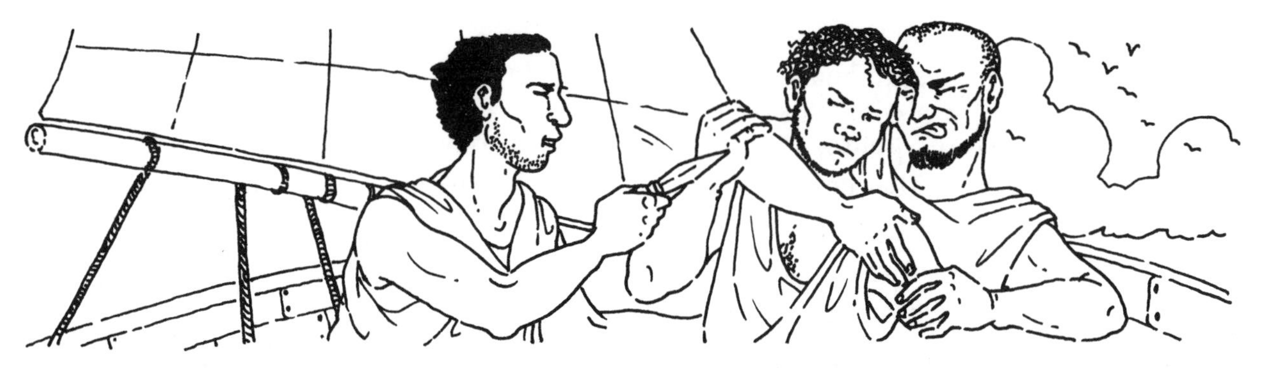

Around 75BC, long before he became dictator of the Roman Empire, Julius Caesar decided to go for a holiday on the island of Rhodes. But on the way there the ship was taken by pirates. One of the robbers recognised Caesar, and the pirates decided to keep Caesar alive and demand a ransom. Caesar asked how much ransom they would demand. When they told him, he was shocked. It was not enough. A man of Caesar's greatness was worth a huge ransom. He told them to demand at least fifty talents of gold.

The pirates did as Caesar told them. They sent his servants to ask for the ransom, and locked him up below deck with his doctor and two servants.

It took Caesar's servants forty days to return with the ransom. By this time the young Roman was getting tired of sitting in a smelly cabin.

The pirates kept their part of the deal and released Caesar. But as they did so, Caesar told them that he would find them and nail each one to a tree. The pirates laughed at the young man's words.

But shortly after his release, Caesar gathered some soldiers and hunted them down. When he caught them, he cut their throats and had them all nailed to trees just as he had promised. Then he went for his holiday in Rhodes.

From *Pirates and Treasure* by Saviour Pirotta

Answer these questions in sentences.
Write the answers in your book.

1 What was the reason for Julius Caesar's journey?
2 What happened on the way?
3 Why didn't the pirates kill Julius Caesar?
4 Why was Julius Caesar shocked?
5 Where did Caesar have to wait to be released?
6 How much ransom did the pirates demand?
7 What happened when the ransom was paid?
8 Why do you think the pirates laughed at Caesar's threat?
9 What happened in the end?

10 If you had to choose another title for the story, which of these would be best?
Caesar's Holiday **The Pirate Ship** **Caesar's Revenge**

11 Find a word in the story that means the same, or nearly the same, as each of the words below.
ask **captured** **fame** **ruler** **knew** **bargain**

Name ______________________ Date ______________

Helen Keller

Helen was not a pleasant child. By the time she was five years old, her parents were in despair and didn't know what to do with her. If she was cross or couldn't have her own way she kicked, screamed and threw her food around the room, and even hit her mother and father. They could not take her out and their family and friends wouldn't visit them because Helen was so badly behaved.

Helen had been a beautiful baby. She had smiled and laughed a lot, and had begun to walk and talk; she had been her parents' pride and joy when she was born in the small town of Tuscumbia, U.S.A. But when she was eighteen months old, Helen had been very ill and the illness had left her blind and deaf. As she could not hear, she could not learn to talk. It must have been very frightening to live in a dark, silent world. Her parents felt sorry for her and spoiled her. They did everything for her except to teach her how to behave, which is why she was such an unpleasant child.

No one seemed able to help until they found a young teacher called Anne Sullivan. The first thing that Anne did was to make Helen do as she was told and behave properly. It was not easy and Anne had to be very firm with her, but she was loving too.

After a month or so Anne began to teach Helen the deaf and dumb alphabet, but it was very difficult because Helen was also blind.

Helen was a very intelligent child and learned quickly. She soon learned how to read Braille, a system of dots which blind people "read" with their fingers. Slowly she came out of her silent world, for now she was able to "talk" with her fingers and others could "talk" to her. A whole new world opened up to her.

Helen then went to a special school where she learned to "speak" and "write" in several languages, and she even went on to university.

Helen Keller became famous all over the world as someone who could overcome the most difficult obstacles. She visited many different countries to encourage other people to follow her example and never give up hope.

True or false?
In your book, copy out the sentences which are true.

1. Helen was very ill when she was eighteen months old.
2. Helen was born in Ireland.
3. Helen was spoiled by her parents.
4. Helen was blind and deaf.
5. Helen always had friends to play.
6. Helen learned to "speak" and "write" in several languages.
7. Braille is a system of reading by feeling raised dots on the page.
8. Helen was well behaved.
9. Tuscumbia is a town in America.
10. The person who helped Helen was called Anne Sullivan.
11. Helen learned to "speak" with her fingers.
12. Helen was not an intelligent child.
13. Anne Sullivan always let Helen have her own way.
14. It is easy for someone who is blind to learn the deaf and dumb alphabet.

Name ______________________________ Date ______________

Sunk!

The watchers on the shore were stunned into silence. What they had witnessed seemed impossible. The great ship, the *Mary Rose,* pride of the expanding English navy, had slowly sunk lower in the water and slipped beneath the waves of Portsmouth Harbour.

All eyes shifted nervously towards King Henry VIII, who, together with his friends, advisers and various invited ambassadors, had come on this summer day in 1545 to admire his favourite vessel. They had watched as his navy sailed proudly out from Portsmouth to fight the French invasion fleet, which was more than three times its size. But before a shot had been fired the day had turned into a disaster. The King was horrified; this ship had been built specially for him with 207 guns, and carried 500 men.

It had sunk without warning. Many pairs of eyes watched anxiously for signs of survivors, but only 30 men succeeded in escaping from the doomed ship.

The King demanded answers from his advisers: how and why did the *Mary Rose* sink?

It is believed that the ship was simply overloaded. The weight of cannons, men, weapons, armour and stores was too great and not evenly spread. Part of the ship was too low in the water, so waves may have washed in through the gun ports and made the ship tip over with the extra weight of the water.

It was a great shock for the King to lose such a ship, and a tragedy to lose so many men.

But 437 years later, in 1982, what had been a disaster for King Henry VIII became a triumph for marine archaeologists and historians. After much planning and preparation, they succeeded in raising the *Mary Rose* from the mud of the seabed.

Not only did they save part of the ship, but they also found many objects which help to give a picture of the tools and everyday items that were used at the time, as well as the skeletons of the seamen.

The *Mary Rose* and the objects found preserved inside her are all on display in a museum in Portsmouth.

Answer these questions in sentences.
Write the answers in your book.

1. Why were the people on the shore so shocked?
2. Which king was watching the fleet?
3. In what year did this event take place?
4. Why was the English fleet setting sail?
5. How many men and guns did the *Mary Rose* have on board?
6. What might have caused the *Mary Rose* to sink?
7. How did the King feel as he watched the *Mary Rose* go down?
8. How long did the *Mary Rose* lie on the seabed?
9. What did the archaeologists find in the wreck of the *Mary Rose?*
10. Where is the *Mary Rose* now?

Name ______________________ Date ______________

A letter to Rome

Cumae
31st August AD79

Greetings, brother Marcus!

You may be surprised to receive this letter from me as you must have heard news about the destruction of our fine city, Pompeii, some days ago. Perhaps you think us dead? Well, brother, we are numbered among the few survivors favoured by the gods. Livia and the children are safe here with me in the small town of Cumae.

Our chief servant, Septimus, and all his family are here with us, though some of the other servants could not be persuaded to leave and have undoubtedly perished.

It is thanks to Septimus that we are alive. What we considered to be innocent rumblings and grumblings from our old mountain, Vesuvius, had greater significance for Septimus. An old aunt of his was a soothsayer and she had warned him of the danger from the mountain. Although he took little notice at the time, he remembered her predictions and respected her skills.

On that morning, when the ground began to shake and Vesuvius began to smoke and rumble, Septimus harnessed the cart immediately and bundled his family into it. He convinced me that time was short, so Livia and the children clambered in too, whilst I followed behind in my chariot. We left everything behind except Livia's jewels and my money pouch, and we sped out through the city gates and away to safety.

As we looked back, we saw flames spurting from the mountainside and thick clouds of ash and cinders rolling down to engulf the city. Boiling mud and lava flowed down, covering everything in their path including the poor souls who had delayed too long.

We reached the safety of Cumae, and are staying here for another few days. Then we will begin the journey to Rome where we will settle. Will you provide a roof over our heads, brother, until we can have a house built?

Septimus and I returned to Pompeii on the third day when the mountain had settled. There is nothing left, no sign of our great city, just the grey mountainside under a blanket of ash and mud, littered with rocks. There is nothing left for us here now.

Vale!
Your brother Claudius

1 Read these sentences carefully, and then write them out in the correct order.

- **a)** Flames spurted from the mountain.
- **b)** Septimus bundled his family into the cart.
- **c)** Claudius and his family reached safety in Cumae.
- **d)** The ground shook and Vesuvius began to rumble and smoke.
- **e)** Ash, cinders, lava and mud covered everything.
- **f)** A soothsayer warned of danger from the mountain.
- **g)** Claudius put Livia and the children on the cart and followed in his chariot.

Answer these questions in sentences.
Write the answers in your book.

2 What relation was Claudius to Marcus?
3 What means of transport did they use to escape?
4 Where did Claudius and his family find safety?
5 Where did they intend to make a new life?

Name ______________________ Date ______________

Beware of the Gobbler!

As the sun was setting, Tanus the scribe and his wife Nofra were finishing their evening meal of goose, vegetables and fresh fruit. Their children Hapti and Lostris were playing with their cat and her litter of kittens in the courtyard of their home, which stood on the banks of the great River Nile.

"Are you ready for your bedtime story?" Nofra called to the children. They came and settled closer to their parents.

"Please tell us about the Gobbler," begged the children.

So Tanus got out a large sheet of papyrus; because he was a scribe, he had been able to write this story in hieroglyphs or picture writing. He read them a story that was told to children all over Egypt to teach them to be honest and kind and to stand up for what was right:

"One sad day, a lovely lady called Tati became very ill and died. After her body had been prepared, it was placed in a tomb. But the spirit of Tati was going on to the afterlife. The way to the afterlife (or Blessed Fields) is not easy, so the Book of the Dead was placed in her tomb to help her on her way. This book told her the right spells and passwords to use to escape from the giant snakes and other creatures that would try to stop her.

"After crossing the River of Death and completing the long, dangerous journey, Tati came to the room where the gods would give her her last great test.

"The god Osiris and his wife were sitting on their thrones. In the middle of the room was a huge pair of scales with the jackal-headed god Anubis beside them – waiting. Thoth, the ibis-headed god of wisdom, was the scribe; he took notes of what happened. In the corner, looking hopeful, sat a huge creature – part crocodile, part lion and part hippopotamus – the Gobbler! Tati did not dare to look at this creature.

"Maat, the goddess of truth and justice, led Tati to the scales. Anubis placed Tati's heart on one side of the scales and a feather on the other. All the gods and goddesses asked Tati if she had led a good life without hurting or upsetting other people. Tati replied that she had done her best. They all waited while Anubis weighed her heart against the Feather of Truth. If her heart was lighter than the feather, it meant that she had been good and could go into the Blessed Fields. If her heart was heavier than the feather, it meant that she had not lived a good life and the Gobbler would pounce on her and eat her.

"The gods and goddesses smiled and the Gobbler slunk back to his corner. Tati's heart was lighter than the feather! They welcomed her into the Blessed Fields where she would be happy for ever. Here there was sunshine, food, plants and flowers, and no one was ever poor or ill."

Tanus reminded the children that this story held a lesson for everyone. Hapti and Lostris smiled sleepily and went happily off to bed.

Answer these questions in sentences.
Write the answers in your book.

1. What time of day was it when Tanus told the story?
2. Where did the family live?
3. What were the names of the children?
4. What job did Tanus do?
5. Did the family have any pets?
6. What did they eat for their evening meal?
7. What did her family put in Tati's tomb to help her on her way?
8. What was Tati's last great test?
9. Who weighed her heart?
10. Who was the god of wisdom?
11. Who was disappointed with the results of the test?
12. Why did the gods and goddesses smile?
13. What were the Blessed Fields?
14. What would be our name for the Blessed Fields?
15. What did this story teach the children?

Name ______________________ Date ______________

The Elizabethan Echo

1588

ARMADA DEFEATED! ENGLAND SAVED!

News has been received of our navy's great victory over the Spanish fleet!

The great Armada sent by King Philip of Spain to invade our land has suffered a humiliating defeat.

Since the death of our own Queen Mary I, Philip of Spain, who was her husband, has held to his belief that he should be King of England. He devised a cunning plan to send a great fleet up the English Channel to dock at the French port of Calais. There they would take on an army of soldiers who would cross the Channel and invade Britain. But his plan did not go well.

Admiral Lord Howard, Sir Francis Drake and John Hawkins heard of these plans, and our fleet gathered at Plymouth where it was thought that the Spanish would invade. On sighting the Armada, beacon fires were lit across the countryside. The English fleet set out quickly and met the invaders near the Isle of Wight before the Armada could reach Calais. After savage fighting, the Spanish ships raced for Calais to await their soldiers. That night, some old English vessels were filled with tar and gunpowder, set on fire and steered towards the Spanish fleet lying near Calais.

The Armada scattered but some Spanish ships were rammed by the blazing vessels. Our ships then gave battle. The Spaniards could not withstand the attack; some of their ships were destroyed and others damaged by severe storms as they fled northwards.

King Philip has lost half his navy. Our navy – under such brave seamen as Admiral Lord Howard, Sir Francis Drake and John Hawkins – is victorious!

ENGLAND IS SAVED! GOD SAVE THE QUEEN!

Answer these questions in sentences.
Write the answers in your book.

1 Which king was intending to invade England?
2 Why did he believe he should be King of England?
3 Which French port was the Armada making for?
4 Why were they going to this port?
5 What was the signal that the Armada had been sighted?
6 Where did the English fleet sail from?
7 Where did the English fleet meet the Armada?
8 How was the Spanish fleet scattered near Calais?
9 How were other Spanish ships destroyed?
10 Who were the brave seamen mentioned in the story?

Name ______________________ Date ______________

The Festival of the Tooth

In a small village on the borders of India and Nepal, long before the birth of Jesus, Queen Maya gave birth to a son called Siddhartha Gautama.

His father the King wanted his son to become a great ruler, but the gods knew otherwise. When he had grown up, he left his comfortable life at the palace and lived as a monk. He travelled all over India, teaching the people to be content with life and at peace with themselves. He was known as the Buddha, "the Enlightened One". Many people follow his teaching today. Buddhists follow the "Eightfold Path" which gives a set of eight rules for leading a good life.

Kandy is a beautiful city in Sri Lanka. It is built round the edge of a lake. On a small hill is a great temple which was built specially to house a relic of the Buddha – his tooth. The tooth can never be seen; it is kept deep inside many caskets. But once a year, in August, on the night of the full moon, there is a special procession for it.

First to come are the elephants. They wear brilliant gold head-dresses covered with silver studs and coloured glass to look like jewels. The biggest elephant carries a pagoda, and in it rests the casket with the tooth. There is great excitement among all the watching crowds when it is seen. The tooth is carried at slow elephant pace right round the city. Some elephants wear bright cloths on their backs, and others are painted all over. Each has its mahmout (driver), also dressed up. Following them come dancers and fire swallowers. Then another row of elephants (there are many in Sri Lanka). Fireworks go up and the festival, which is called the peharera, continues all night.

From *The Buddhist World* by Anne Bancroft

Answer these questions in sentences.
Write the answers in your book.

1. Where was the Buddha born?
2. Who was his mother?
3. What was his real name?
4. What does the word "Buddha" mean?
5. How many rules do Buddhists follow?
6. In which city is the Buddha's tooth kept?
7. Which four facts do you know about this city?
8. When is the procession held?
9. How is the tooth taken round the city?
10. Describe what the elephants look like.
11. What other activities are there during the festival?

Name ______________________ Date ______________

Bring Out Your Dead!

Samuel huddled down in his bed. Just after midnight he heard the clanging of the bell and the mournful cry: "Bring out your dead!"

He listened to the shuffling footsteps and the hushed voices as the bodies of those who had died during the day were loaded on to the cart. The wheels rattled over the cobbles as the cart moved to the next street. Again, there came the dreaded words: "Bring out your dead!"

It was September 1665 and the plague was at its peak. Thousands were dying in London every day, and in Samuel's home, as in many others, the family lived in fear of falling sick with the plague. Samuel's mother watched her family anxiously, hoping they would not develop the shivering, fever and cough that were the first signs.

The next evening, Sam watched his mother quietly sewing, the flickering candle making strange shadows on the wall.

"Do you think Benjamin is sick?" he asked. Benjamin was his best friend.

His mother did not reply. She knew there was a large red cross on Benjamin's door and a watchman placed outside. No one was allowed in or out of the house for forty days, by which time the people inside would be either cured or dead.

Benjamin's mother sighed. The rich people had all fled the city to escape the plague. The King had moved to Nonsuch in Surrey. Only the poor were left.

"Do you think Benjamin is sick?" Sam asked again.

"I hope not," she replied uneasily.

In your book, write down one word from the passage that means the same as each of these words.

1 **ringing**
2 **sad**
3 **quiet**
4 **shambling**
5 **height**
6 **worriedly**
7 **symptoms**
8 **better**
9 **run away from**

Read the passage again and think carefully about how you would have felt if you had lived at the time of the plague. Now answer these questions in sentences. Write the answers in your book.

10 Why do you think the dead were collected after midnight?
11 How did Samuel's mother know that someone in Benjamin's house was sick?
12 What were the first symptoms of the plague?
13 Why didn't the poor people leave the city?

Crowded streets, scurrying feet,
Smells and dirt, be alert!
Rats and fleas spread disease!

14 Read the following statements and write down those which help explain why the plague spread so quickly.

a) Many of the poor people had a poor diet.
b) The King left London.
c) Disease spreads quickly in a crowded city.
d) Many rats lived in the cities and towns.
e) Many people died.
f) Fleas from the rats bit people and spread the disease.
g) The dead were taken away in carts.

Name ______________________ Date ____________

A Special Meal

Ruth and Nathan were dressed in their best clothes. They were waiting for Uncle Len and Auntie Rosalea to arrive. Today was a special day; it was the day when Jewish people celebrate the feast of the Passover or Pesach.

The Passover reminds people of the time long ago when the Jewish people, or Israelites as they were called, were slaves of the cruel Pharaoh in Egypt. God told Moses that he must persuade the Pharaoh to let the Israelites go, and then God would lead them to a land of their own. Moses went to the Pharaoh and demanded the Israelites' freedom, but the Pharaoh would not agree. Moses threatened that God would send plagues to Egypt as a punishment, but the Pharaoh was a stubborn man.

Egypt suffered nine horrible plagues: flies, frogs, water turning into blood, darkness and sickness, to name just a few. Sometimes the Pharaoh agreed to let the Israelites go, but then he changed his mind.

The tenth and final plague was dreadful: one night, the first-born son in every Egyptian house was killed by the Angel of Death.

The Israelite families escaped this because Moses had told them to paint crosses on their doors with the blood of a lamb. The Angel of Death passed over these houses, leaving their inhabitants unharmed.

That night, the Israelites ate a meal of lamb and bread and then prepared to leave Egypt.

Next day the Pharaoh, whose eldest son had been killed, let Moses and the Israelites leave, but even then he did not keep his promise. He chased them, but the Israelites were saved when the Red Sea opened to let them pass, drowning the Egyptians who tried to follow.

So Moses led his people out of Egypt to find the Promised Land.

Since then, Jewish people have celebrated Passover every spring. There is a special Passover meal called Seder. All the food has a special meaning to remind people of the Israelites' escape from Egypt. There is lamb (the blood of a lamb was used to paint crosses on the Israelites' doors), bitter herbs (for the misery of slavery), an egg (to represent new life), a green vegetable (for spring), and charoset, a mixture of nuts, apples, raisins and wine (for the sweetness of freedom). There is also a bowl of salt water on the table (for the Israelites' tears of sorrow during their slavery).

The whole meal is a celebration of a wonderful story: the story of escape and a new life in the Promised Land.

Answer these questions in sentences.
Write the answers in your book.

1. What special celebration were Ruth and Nathan looking forward to?
2. The Jewish people were slaves in which land?
3. What order did God give to Moses?
4. What did God promise the Jewish people?
5. Why did God send the plagues to Egypt?
6. What was the final plague?
7. How did the Israelites escape this plague?
8. What did the Pharaoh do?
9. How did the Israelites cross the Red Sea?
10. What is the Passover meal called?
11. List three things eaten at the Seder and explain what each one stands for.
12. Draw a picture to illustrate the story.

Name ______________________ Date ______________

The Princess and the Parlourmaid

A story about a princess is being told to a little girl called Hannah by her mother Lilly, who used to be a parlourmaid in a big house.

" 'Hello,' said an inquisitive voice. 'Who are you, pray?'

'I'm Lilly, Miss,' I said. I could tell she wasn't a servant by the way she spoke.

'I'm Drina, and I should like you to talk to me.'

What she was doing up at that late hour, I don't know.

'Oh, I'm not allowed to talk to the likes of you, Miss,' I said. 'I'm only a maid.'

'Then I command you to!' said the Princess playfully. She had a doll on her lap, most beautifully dressed. She told me it was her best friend."

"Didn't she have brothers or sisters?" asked Hannah.

"There was Charlie, her stepbrother, but he lived in Germany, and her stepsister, Fedore, was much older than her."

"What about her governess?" asked Hannah.

"Louise Lehzen was her governess. Drina adored her, but they'd had a row that day... Lehzen insisted on pinning a sprig of holly under Drina's chin to remind her to hold her head up like a queen."

"Did her know she was going to be Queen one day?"

"No, darling, not then. Her 'Uncle King' was still on the throne. She said he was fat and wore greasy make-up to hide his wrinkles. We giggled so much, we had to stuff our fists in our mouths in case the Butler heard us."

"I told the Princess I'd better go, saying I had to be up at five to blacklead the range.

'What's blackleading the range?' she wanted to know. 'It sounds fun! I've got to do horrid algebra and deportment. I'd much rather go for a ride on Dicky the Donkey. Uncle York gave him to me.' She asked me to meet her in secret after tea, and we'd drive to the chestnut trees and back."

"Did you go?" asked Hannah innocently.

Her mother shook her head. "I was on my knees with exhaustion. The Housekeeper had me scrubbing floors until my knuckles bled. She had a fondness for gin and could be cruel. We used to call her Pug."

"Poor Mamma!" said Hannah. "Weren't you jealous of all Drina's lovely things?"

"No," said her mother. "We were poor, but we were never lonely. The Princess would have swapped all the silver spoons in the palace for a true friend."

Drina became Queen Victoria at the age of eighteen when her uncle, King William IV, died. Queen Victoria ruled for 64 years, from 1837 to 1901.

From *The Princess and the Parlourmaid* by Jeanne Willis

Answer these questions in sentences.
Write the answers in your book.

1. How did Lilly know that Drina wasn't a servant?
2. Why wasn't Lilly allowed to talk to Drina?
3. Who was Drina's best friend?
4. Why had Drina quarrelled with her governess?
5. Why did Drina and Lilly try to keep quiet?
6. Why didn't Lilly meet Drina after tea?
7. Why did Lilly feel sorry for Drina?
8. Match each of the words in List **A** to the word with the closest meaning in list **B**.

A	**B**
inquisitive	**teacher**
command	**tiredness**
governess	**curious**
exhaustion	**order**

Name ______________________ Date ______________

Louis Braille

On 4th January 1809, in a small town near Paris, the Braille family were celebrating the birth of their fourth child. It was a boy and they named him Louis.

Louis grew up to be a bright boy with blond curls, adored by his older brother and sisters. His father made leather saddles and harnesses, and Louis used to sit in his workshop to watch him. His father often gave him pieces of scrap leather to work with, but Louis was constantly reminded never to touch his father's sharp tools. But one day, when he was alone in the workshop, young Louis tried to copy what he had seen his father do. The sharp knife slipped and cut deeply into his left eye.

His screams of pain brought the family running, but little could be done except to stop the bleeding. The nearest doctor was miles away. Louis then developed an infection in the wound and this spread to his other eye.

Just over a year later, Louis went completely blind. A priest and a teacher took pity on him and gave him lessons. As he had a wonderful memory and did well, he was sent to Paris, to the only school in the country for the blind. Louis was an outstanding pupil, although the type of "writing" then used for the blind was difficult to learn.

Louis decided to invent his own reading and writing system based on raised dots. After finishing his education, he became a teacher at the school, but he was not allowed to use his method of teaching because it was a new idea.

Louis was an excellent teacher and helped many pupils to cope with their blindness, but it was only after his death that Braille writing became popular.

A great deal of good came out of Louis Braille's tragic childhood accident. His invention has brought help and hope to blind people all over the world.

Answer these questions in sentences.
Write the answers in your book.

1 How many children were there in the Braille family?
2 What was the strict rule that Louis had to remember when he was in his father's workshop?
3 How did Louis become blind?

4 Use a dictionary or thesaurus to find a word or words meaning the same as each of these.

adored	**scrap**
infection	**outstanding**
method	**cope**
system	**tragic**

Name ______________________________ Date ______________

Arthur and Excalibur

Arthur became King of England when he pulled the sword Excalibur from a huge block of stone. Only the rightful King was able to do this.

Arthur gathered the Knights of the Round Table and together they set off to war once again. And again it happened that Arthur and his Knights came to no harm. With his magic sword in his hand, he and his companions won every battle and frightened off their enemies.

All his success in battle went to King Arthur's head. "We are the conquerors," he shouted to his cheering Knights after the battle. "I cannot be beaten!" he said quietly to himself. He hardly gave the Lady of the Lake a thought.

One day, Queen Guinevere was sitting in the window of her room at Camelot. She was working on some fine embroidery for Excalibur's velvet cover. Guinevere had almost finished her work and was carefully sewing the last threads. She stitched her embroidery on to the velvet cover and was about to put the sword inside it. But as she touched the sword, she caught sight of the Lady of the Lake!

"Guinevere," cried the wise woman. "You are the King's faithful wife, so I give you a warning! If Arthur ever forgets that it is only the magic sword which gives him his powers, it will be taken from him again. He will be killed by his own nephew Mordred."

Guinevere let out a cry of horror as the Lady of the Lake vanished.

From then on, Guinevere anxiously watched her beloved husband's every move. She stayed close to him when he came back to Camelot after his battles. Soon she noticed a dangerous change happening to Arthur. He had got used to winning and had become proud and vain. Even his subjects started saying: "Nobody can do any harm to Arthur. He is almost like a god."

Arthur had forgotten Excalibur and the Lady of the Lake.

From *Arthur and Excalibur* by Angelika Lukesch

Answer these questions in sentences.
Write the answers in your book.

1 How did Arthur become King?
2 How did King Arthur's success affect him?
3 What was Queen Guinevere doing?
4 Who appeared in the room?
5 What was the warning?
6 What was Queen Guinevere's reaction?
7 What relation was Arthur to Mordred?
8 Which of these words best describe King Arthur?

arrogant	**boastful**	**proud**
timid	**plump**	**cowardly**
thoughtless	**humble**	**vain**

9 Which of these words best describe Queen Guinevere?

anxious	**restless**	**loving**
cruel	**lazy**	**faithful**
patient	**careful**	**selfish**

10 What did the people think of their King?

Name ______________________________ Date ______________

The Great Fire of London

London Weekly News – Monday 7th September 1666

In the early hours of Sunday morning, a great tragedy struck our beloved city. A few sparks from the oven started a small fire in the baker's shop in Pudding Lane and it quickly took hold. The flying sparks from the blaze were blown by a strong easterly wind, and set fire to the dry timbers of the inn in Fish Street Hill, catching light to the stables and the straw within.

The inferno quickly spread, racing through the narrow streets and destroying both houses and churches. The great storehouses on the banks of the Thames with their wine, oil and tar were quickly caught by the blaze, and a huge cloud of smoke and soot hung over the city.

Our brave citizens formed human chains to fight the flames with pails of water. Many were seen running from their burning homes carrying what possessions they could, while the more fortunate saved their families and household goods on handcarts. The good ferrymen rowed many victims to the other side of the river or further upstream to escape the flames. It is said that even the river water was boiling. Those fleeing by river also noted that swarms of rats were seen running from the flames of the city and leaping into the Thames. The bodies of rats littered the surface of the water.

Even St. Paul's Cathedral and the Guildhouse have been burned. After the fires had raged for three days, desperate action had to be taken. The King himself came to view the devastation, and the Mayor has ordered that certain houses be blown up by the use of gunpowder. Our citizens were frightened by the explosions but it is hoped to create gaps so that the fire cannot spread. Our city has lost 84 of its churches, and 13,000 homes have been destroyed. Many of our good citizens who have lost their homes are camping outside the city walls. It is provident that the weather is mild or their plight would be much worse. We must learn from this catastrophe, and future homes must be built of bricks and stone and London's streets made wider.

1 Write these sentences, in the correct order, in your book.

- **a)** Citizens formed human chains with buckets of water.
- **b)** In future, homes were to be built of stone and brick and the streets would be wider.
- **c)** Sparks started a fire in a baker's shop in Pudding Lane.
- **d)** The long, hot London summer had dried the timbers of the buildings.
- **e)** The fire spread quickly through the narrow lanes of the city.
- **f)** Thousands of houses, many churches and even St. Paul's Cathedral were destroyed.

2 Find a word in the story which means the same as each of these words.

belongings **disaster** **blaze** **lucky** **warm** **troubles**

Name ______________________ Date ______________

The Secret Room

Anne crept close to the window. The curtains were tightly drawn, but through a little hole in one of them, Anne could see into the street below.

"Come away, Anne," said her mother sharply. "Someone might see you."

Anne moved away from the window. She knew it was not a wise thing to do.

For months now, Anne Frank, aged thirteen, her mother, father and elder sister Margot had lived in a set of hidden rooms on the top floor of an office block in Amsterdam after fleeing from Germany. Four more people lived with them. They were all Jewish and were hiding from the Germans, who had invaded Holland and who were hunting all the Jews. The Germans, led by Adolf Hitler, hated Jews and were sending them to concentration camps where they were murdered or died of starvation and disease.

Anne's father had prepared this hiding place and had found friends who would bring them food and keep their secret. The entrance to the hiding place was well hidden behind a bookcase in a top floor room. The rooms were very small and cramped for eight people, and they were short of food. They had to be silent during the day for fear of people hearing them.

We know about their life because Anne wrote a wonderful diary in a notebook which she called Kitty.

They spent two years in hiding, which was especially hard for two friendly, lively girls. In June 1944 they heard that British and American troops were driving back the Germans from France. They were delighted – soon they too would be free!

But on August 4th 1944 came the sound they had hoped they would never hear – the crashing of boots and men shouting in German. Someone had betrayed them. They were arrested and sent on the last train to the concentration camps.

Edith Frank died of starvation, and Anne and Margot both caught typhus. Margot died first, and Anne a few days later.

The only survivor was Anne's father. After the war was over, he returned to Amsterdam, and one of his friends gave him his daughter's diary. He had found it on the floor of the secret room after the family had been arrested.

The diary of Anne Frank tells the story of a very brave fifteen year-old girl who suffered terrible hardship and died tragically so near the end of the war.

Use the story of Anne Frank to solve the crossword.

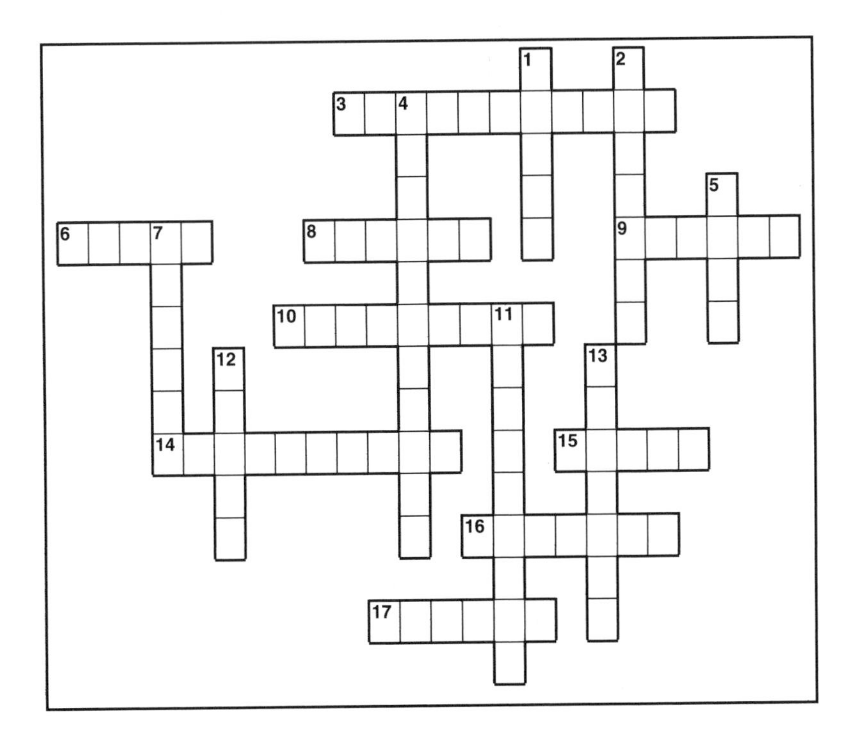

Clues for ACROSS

3 The name of the German leader
6 The name of Anne's diary
8 The religion of the Frank family
9 The month of their capture
10 The city where they lived
14 Edith Frank died of this
15 Where Kitty was found
16 The only survivor
17 They had to be__________ during the day.

Clues for DOWN

1 The number of people in the secret room
2 The country from which they had fled
4 Where the secret room was
5 The month their hopes were raised
7 Margot and Anne died of this.
11 The name of the main character in this story
12 They travelled on this to the concentration camp.
13 The country they had fled to

Name ______________________ Date ______________

Invasion!

In the year 55BC, 55 years before Jesus was born, Julius Caesar came to Britain with a small fleet of ships. He sent men into the countryside and they reported to him that the land was green and fertile, and food was plentiful. There were people who could be taken as slaves, and minerals such as gold, silver, iron and tin could be taken from the ground.

Julius Caesar decided that he would go back to Rome, gather a greater fleet and many soldiers and invade Britain. He tried this the following year, with limited success. Although he defeated some of the tribes in southern Britain and took some prisoners back to Rome as slaves, he had to abandon his attempt.

It was not until AD43 that the Romans gathered a large enough army to conquer Britain, under the Emperor Claudius. One of the worst battles was at Colchester where a British leader called Caractacus was captured and taken to Rome.

The Romans were good rulers and built new roads, houses, bridges and forts. They encouraged the Britons to live in a more civilised way.

But the Roman army had to work hard to keep their power. Queen Boudicca, leader of the Iceni tribe in eastern Britain, led a rebellion against the Romans. The Romans defeated her, and Boudicca poisoned herself rather than be captured.

The tribes of Scotland led many raids against the Romans and so, in AD122, the Emperor Hadrian ordered the Roman army to build a great wall across the north of England to separate the land under Roman rule from these fierce tribes. This wall was named Hadrian's Wall, and some parts of it can still be seen today, together with the ruins of some of the forts which were built along the wall.

Legions of soldiers were stationed in the forts, ready to go out and defend Roman Britain from attack.

The Romans ruled Britain for over 400 years, but then their armies left to fight in Europe. The British were left to defend themselves, and much of the good that the Romans did was lost.

Answer these questions in sentences.
Write the answers in your book.

1 List the reasons why Julius Caesar decided that he would invade Britain.
2 Why didn't he try to invade in 55BC?
3 What did Julius Caesar achieve in 54BC?
4 How long was it until Emperor Claudius invaded Britain?
5 List some of the improvements the Romans made in Britain.
6 Who was the woman who led a rebellion against the Romans?
7 Why did Hadrian order a wall to be built?
8 Why did the Romans leave Britain?

Name ______________________ Date ______________

Invasion! (continued)

9 Use the story of the Roman invasion to solve the crossword.

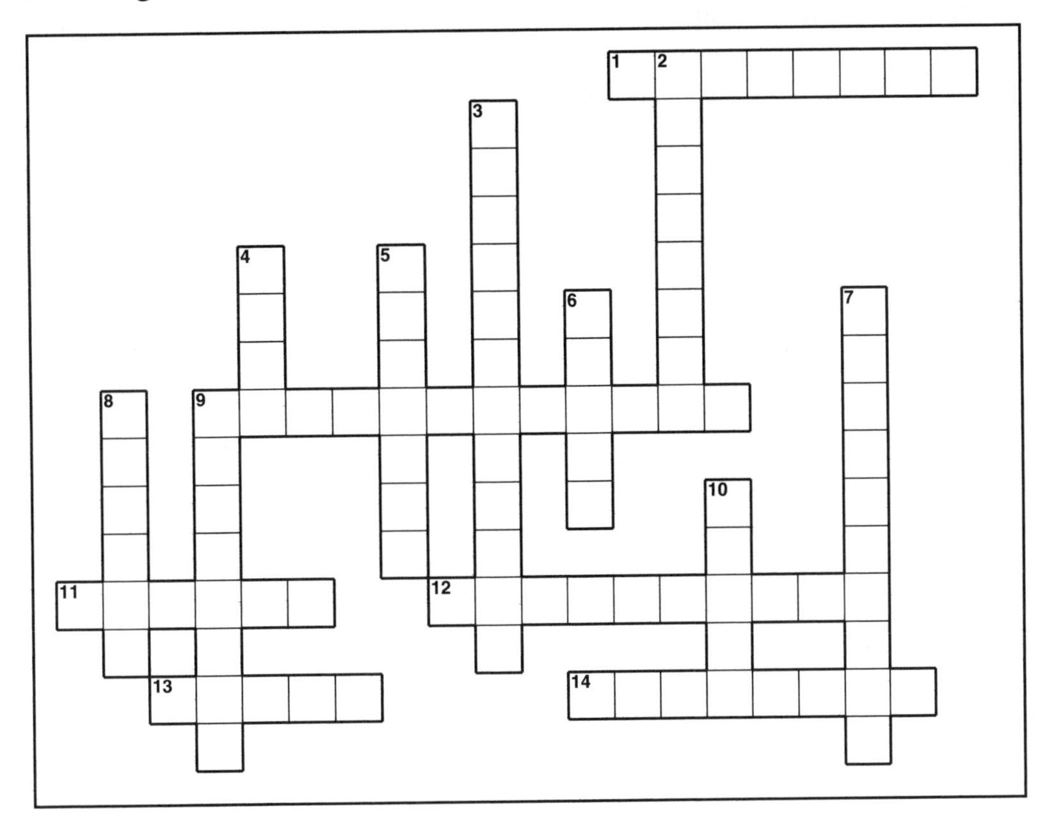

Clues for ACROSS

1 Tribes from this country attacked the Romans.
9 The meaning of "BC"
11 The name given to a group of Roman soldiers
12 The name of the leader who was captured
13 A tribe who lived in eastern Britain
14 Boudicca did this to herself rather than be captured.

Clues for DOWN

2 The name of the Roman Emperor who conquered Britain
3 The name of the Roman leader who came to Britain in 55BC.
4 The place the invaders came from
5 The name of the Emperor who ordered the wall to be built
6 The soldiers lived in these on the wall.
7 A large battle took place here.
8 The Romans would take the people as ________.
9 The name of the leader of the eastern tribe
10 One of the important things that the Romans built

Name ______________________________ Date ______________

Death of a Pharaoh

"Tell them it is ready."

This was the important message that Halim was taking from his master, Menset, to the palace. He ran along the dusty streets and presented himself to the palace guards. He gave his master's name and they escorted him to the inner rooms where the family of the dead Pharaoh were waiting with the nobles and priests and the Vizier. Halim knelt, pressed his forehead to the tiled floor, and then looked up and gave his message. This was the signal for the final preparations for the burial of the dead Pharaoh, Tutankhamun, to begin.

Halim's master, Menset, was an embalmer. For more than 70 days since Tutankhamun's death he had been preparing the body for mummification. First it was washed in palm oil, then most of the internal organs were removed and placed in separate stone jars. After filling the body with linen pads and perfumed herbs and spices, he stitched it up and then covered it with natron – a kind of salt. After about 60 days the salts had dried the body, and it was cleaned and carefully bound in linen bandages smeared with resin.

Now the mummification was finished and Tutankhamun's family went with the finest goldsmiths to place the golden masks on the mummy. They also took many pieces of precious jewellery to decorate the mummy, and shabti figures and amulets to act as lucky charms. The mummy was then placed in a coffin which was sealed inside two other decorated coffins and put on a sledge drawn by oxen.

A great procession of family, priests, nobles and palace officials formed behind the sledge and wound down to the banks of the Nile. Behind this came many servants carrying the things that were to be buried with Tutankhamun – the possessions that he would need in the afterlife. There were beautifully carved chairs, chests, chariots and statues of gods and goddesses, including two life-sized guards to protect the tomb. In one chest, protected by Anubis, the jackal-headed god of the dead, were four jars containing the Pharaoh's internal organs. Hundreds of smaller objects were also placed in the tomb including bowls of food, pots, jewellery, model boats and even dried flowers.

When they reached the great River Nile, the coffin was placed on a funeral barge and rowed across to the west bank of the city of Thebes. The procession continued from the Nile into the Valley of the Kings where a tomb had been quickly prepared.

It was a small tomb compared to those of other Pharaohs buried here because Tutankhamun had died suddenly and unexpectedly, aged only eighteen. No one knows why he died. The older Pharaohs had had craftsmen working for years to decorate huge tombs for them. The tomb had been cut deep into the hillside. The coffin was taken along a passage and into the burial chamber. It was placed in a stone sarcophagus which was then placed inside four golden cases fitted one inside the other. This was then sealed. The objects to be buried with Tutankhamun were placed carefully in an outer room. Finally, the tomb's entrance was sealed with a slab of rock.

Tutankhamun and his burial treasure were to lie undisturbed in this tomb for over 3,000 years.

Name ______________________ Date ______________

Death of a Pharaoh (continued)

Answer these questions in sentences.
Write the answers in your book.

1 Who brought the message to the palace?
2 What did the message mean?
3 Menset was an embalmer – what did he do?
4 About how long did it take to prepare the body for mummification?
5 List four things that had to be done to mummify a body.
6 Which Pharaoh had died?
7 What did the family place on the mummy?
8 Where was Tutankhamun's tomb?
9 How was Tutankhamun's coffin taken to the tomb?
10 Why were there so many things sealed in the tomb with him?

11 Use the passage about Tutankhamun to solve the crossword.

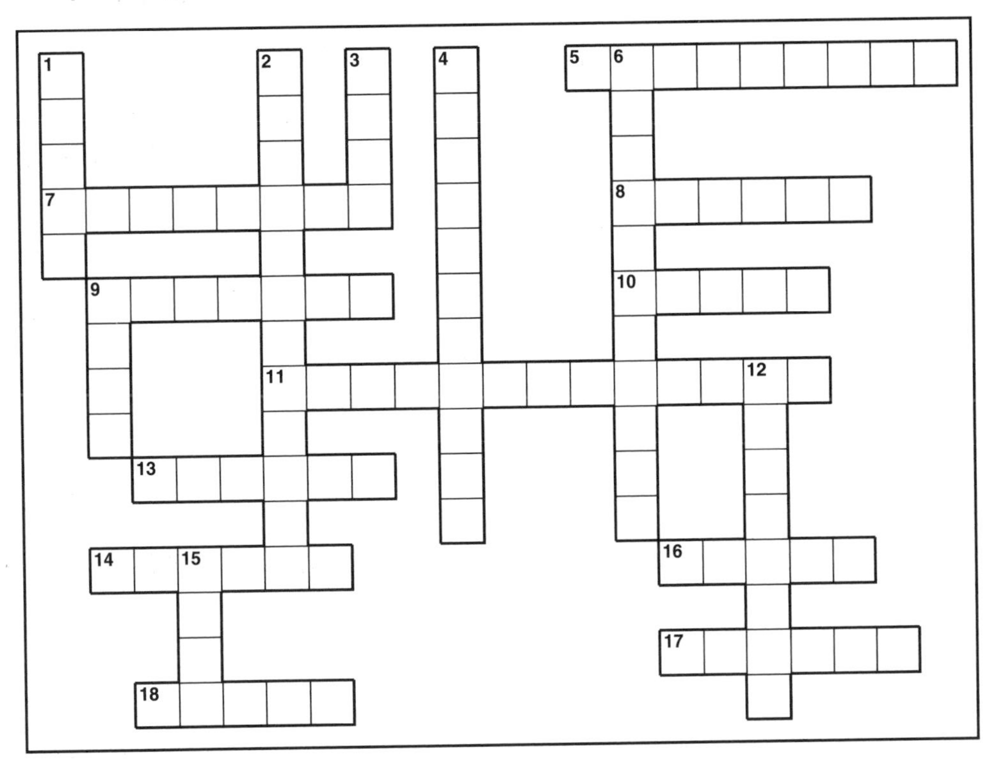

Clues for ACROSS

5 The internal organs were put in these.
7 Tutankhamun's age when he died.
8 Jackal-headed god
9 The name given to the kings of Egypt
10 What Halim did when he delivered the message
11 Room where the coffin was placed
13 A kind of salt
14 Halim's master
16 The name of the messenger
17 The city named in the story
18 The bandages were smeared with this.

Clues for DOWN

1 Material used to bind the body
2 The vessel that carried the coffin across the Nile
3 Animals that drew the sledge
4 The coffin was placed in this.
6 The name of the dead king
9 The oil that the body was washed with
12 Menset's job
15 The main river in Egypt

Name ______________________________ Date ______________

Guru Nanak

Guru Nanak was the founder and first Guru of the Sikh religion. He lived from 1469 to 1539. His most important teachings were that people should live honest, selfless lives and help anyone in need.

Guru Nanak loved to travel. His faithful companion on many of his journeys was a musician called Mardana. On this occasion, Guru Nanak and Mardana had reached the city of Multan, after a long, hot and tiring journey. Mardana was looking forward to a good meal and a long rest, for they had been on the road for almost a week. So, anticipating the comforts ahead, Mardana followed his master through the city gates.

In Guru Nanak's time, the ancient city of Multan was famous far and wide for its priests and holy men. People came from miles around to seek their advice about all manner of things. In return for advice, the people thanked the priests with gifts of money, silk or jewellery. In no time at all, the priests and holy men of Multan grew rich and greedy. When they heard that Guru Nanak was to visit their city, they were not best pleased.

"We don't want him here," one priest said. "He'll be bad for business."

"I agree," said another, "but what can we do to stop him?"

They put their heads together and came up with a plan. It went like this. When Guru Nanak arrived, they would send a messenger to him with a bowl of milk. The bowl would be filled to the brim, so full that not a single drop more would fit in. The message to Guru Nanak would be this:

"There are enough holy men and priests in this city already. And there's no room for any more – not a single one."

The messenger carried the bowl, slowly and carefully, to Guru Nanak. His eyes never left the milk, in case a drop should be spilt. He held the bowl out towards the Guru.

"My masters have sent you this bowl of milk, your Holiness," he said. "Do you have any message for them in return?"

Mardana looked at the bowl of milk. It looked so cool and tempting, and he was so thirsty. He longed for the Guru to take the bowl so they could have a drink. But the Guru didn't. Instead, he stooped down and picked a delicate jasmine flower from a nearby bush, and dropped it into the bowl of milk. The flower filled the bowl of milk with its sweet smell. It was so fragile and light that not a single drop of milk was spilt.

Then the Guru told the messenger, "This is my message for your masters. Just as there is room in this bowl of milk for a jasmine flower to fill it with scent, so there is always room in the world for more goodness and holiness."

Mardana smiled at the Guru's wise words. Going thirsty was a small price to pay. And when the priests and holy men received the Guru's message, they were truly ashamed of their selfish behaviour. They went straight to Guru Nanak to say they were sorry, and to welcome him and Mardana into Multan.

From *Out of the Ark* by Anita Ganieri

Answer these questions in sentences.
Write the answers in your book.

1. Which of the following words would you use to describe Guru Nanak?
   boastful adventurous stubborn kind honest deceitful cowardly wise
2. Why is Guru Nanak famous?
3. Who was Mardana?
4. Why did so many people travel to Multan?
5. Why didn't the priests want Guru Nanak in their city?
6. What did the priests' message to Guru Nanak mean?
7. Why did the messenger carry the bowl so carefully?
8. What did Mardana want to do with the bowl of milk?
9. What did Guru Nanak do with the bowl of milk?
10. What was Guru Nanak's message to the priests?
11. Match each of these words from the story (list **A**) to a word on the same line in list **B**.

A		B	
companion	**friend**	**enemy**	**player**
tiring	**miserable**	**lively**	**exhausting**
manner	**kinds**	**polite**	**choice**
seek	**find**	**discover**	**ask**
tempting	**creamy**	**appealing**	**fruity**
stooped	**turned**	**tumbled**	**bent**
fragile	**pretty**	**delicate**	**awkward**

Name ______________________________ Date ______________

The Unsinkable Ship

"Extra, extra – read all about it! Titanic sinks. Over 1,500 lost."

The unthinkable had happened! The "unsinkable" ship had gone down. The world was stunned by the news.

The *Titanic* set out on her maiden voyage from Southampton to New York on Wednesday 10th April 1912. She was the biggest passenger ship ever built and cost £1,500,000 to build and equip – a huge sum at the time. Her thick steel hull was divided into sixteen watertight compartments. If one compartment should flood, great steel doors would close it off, leaving the rest of the ship safe. Three enormous coal-burning engines would speed the ship across the Atlantic and the very latest technology, the Marconi telegraph radio, would keep her in contact with the rest of the world.

Her owner, J. Bruce Ismay of the White Star Line, had spared no expense in creating a floating palace. There were state rooms, luxurious apartments, gardens, swimming pools and orchestras. Some of the richest people from England and America were on board for the first voyage.

On Sunday 14th April the *Titanic* was speeding through the icy water at 21 knots. There was a radio message from the German ship *Amerika* warning of dangerous icebergs, but the *Titanic* did not reduce speed. At 11.39p.m. the lookout reported a huge iceberg ahead. The helmsman tried to turn the ship away, but it was too late. The hard ice sliced through the hull and six compartments began to fill with icy sea water. Captain Smith knew that with so much damage there was no hope for the ship, and he ordered the radio operator to send the world's first S.O.S. message. It was picked up by the liner *Carpathia* some 80 kilometres away, and she sped to the rescue. Another ship, the *Californian,* was only 30 kilometres away but the radio operator was off-duty and the call was never received.

Bow first, the *Titanic* slowly began to sink. Captain Smith gave the order to abandon ship. There was little panic and the bands kept playing, but then it was realised that there were not enough lifeboats to save everyone. "Women and children first" was the order.

Slowly, the ship slid under the freezing water with over 1,000 passengers still on board. At first light the rescue ships began to arrive, but there were only 705 survivors.

Use a dictionary to find out what these words mean.

1 equip **2 hull** **3 knots** **4 abandon** **5 survivors**

Answer these questions in sentences.
Write the answers in your book.

6 Where was the *Titanic* sailing to?
7 What does "maiden voyage" mean?
8 How many compartments was the hull divided into?
9 What fuel was used for the engines?
10 What does "a floating palace" tell you about the *Titanic?*
11 How many compartments were said to be damaged by the ice?
12 What is an S.O.S. message?
13 Which ship picked up the message?
14 Why didn't the *Californian* come to the rescue?
15 Why couldn't more passengers leave the ship?

Name ______________________________ Date ______________

Crocodile Massacre

The saltwater crocodile is responsible for the biggest ever animal attack on human beings. On 19th February 1945, during the Second World War, 1,000 Japanese soldiers were fleeing from British soldiers who had trapped them on Ramree Island, off the coast of Burma. Their aim was to make it through 30km of mangrove swamp to the safety of the Burmese mainland.

At sunset, the exhausted soldiers stopped for a rest. They tried to keep as quiet as possible, for fear of alerting the British troops. Unfortunately, they weren't quiet enough. During the night, a large pack of saltwater crocs attacked the troops and annihilated them. By the morning there were only 20 survivors.

Bruce Wright, an English naturalist who witnessed the ghastly scene from a barge grounded in the swamp, said later, "From the pitch-black swamp came the sound of shots, punctuated by the screams of wounded men crushed by the jaws of these enormous beasts, and the muffled sounds of the crocodiles harassing them, all producing a hellish cacophony the like of which has rarely been heard on earth."

From *Monsters of the Deep* by Saviour Pirotta

Write down one word from the story that means the same as each of these words.

1 running	**2 ambition**	**3 tired**	**4 warning**	**5 killed**
6 saw	**7 broken**	**8 faint**	**9 plaguing**	**10 noise**

Answer these questions in sentences.
Write the answers in your book.

11 Who were the British soldiers pursuing?
12 Where were the Japanese going?
13 What sort of land did the Japanese have to cross?
14 Why did the Japanese keep quiet?
15 What happened during the night?
16 Why wasn't Bruce Wright hurt?
17 What sounds could be heard?
18 Could anything be seen?

Name ______________________ Date ______________

Doodlebugs

Twickenham News 20th June 1944

Doodlebug survivors

7 dead, 5 injured in V1 attack

Fear is mounting today after reports that a wave of V1 rockets (nicknamed "doodlebugs") was launched against London early yesterday morning.

Many of these deadly rockets fell locally, more than ten miles off their target. The most serious devastation occurred in Water Lane, Twickenham, where a large house converted into four flats was hit and totally demolished. Of the twelve occupants, seven were killed outright and tonight five are in hospital, some seriously injured.

Occupants of one of the flats must be considered particularly fortunate. Fifteen year-old Angela Chandler had a miraculous escape when the whole house blew up around her. She had been in the bathroom preparing for school and was buried under tons of rubble. She was saved from serious injury because she was wedged in a space under her wardrobe. She was conscious throughout the ordeal. She could see cracks of daylight and called to rescuers who worked for hours to dig her out. She astonished doctors by suffering only cuts, bruises and shock, but no broken bones. Her parents, Ann and Bert Chandler, were in the kitchen and were blown into the back garden by the blast. Both were injured, Ann seriously. Their twelve year-old son Peter came home from delivering papers to find his home in ruins; he is being cared for by relatives.

Officials at the War Office state that these new V1 bombs or "doodlebugs" carry nearly one ton of high explosive and can travel at 400 m.p.h.

They are like pilotless planes, and their speed means that air-raid sirens cannot be sounded in time to warn of an attack. They are highly inaccurate, with many falling short of the target. The only warning is the strange noise of the engine, which cuts out as the doodlebug nosedives silently, causing great destruction on impact.

1 Match each of these words from the story (list **A**) to a word on the same line in list **B**.

A	B		
mounting	growing	climbing	riding
occurred	missed	changed	happened
locally	greatly	nearby	correctly
converted	altered	built	moved
miraculous	holy	terrible	amazing
rubble	rocks	bricks	debris
conscious	asleep	awake	injured
astonished	pleased	surprised	horrified
state	announce	shout	insist
silently	quickly	noiselessly	carefully

Name ______________________ Date ______________

Doodlebugs (continued)

2 Use the story of Angela's escape to solve the crossword.

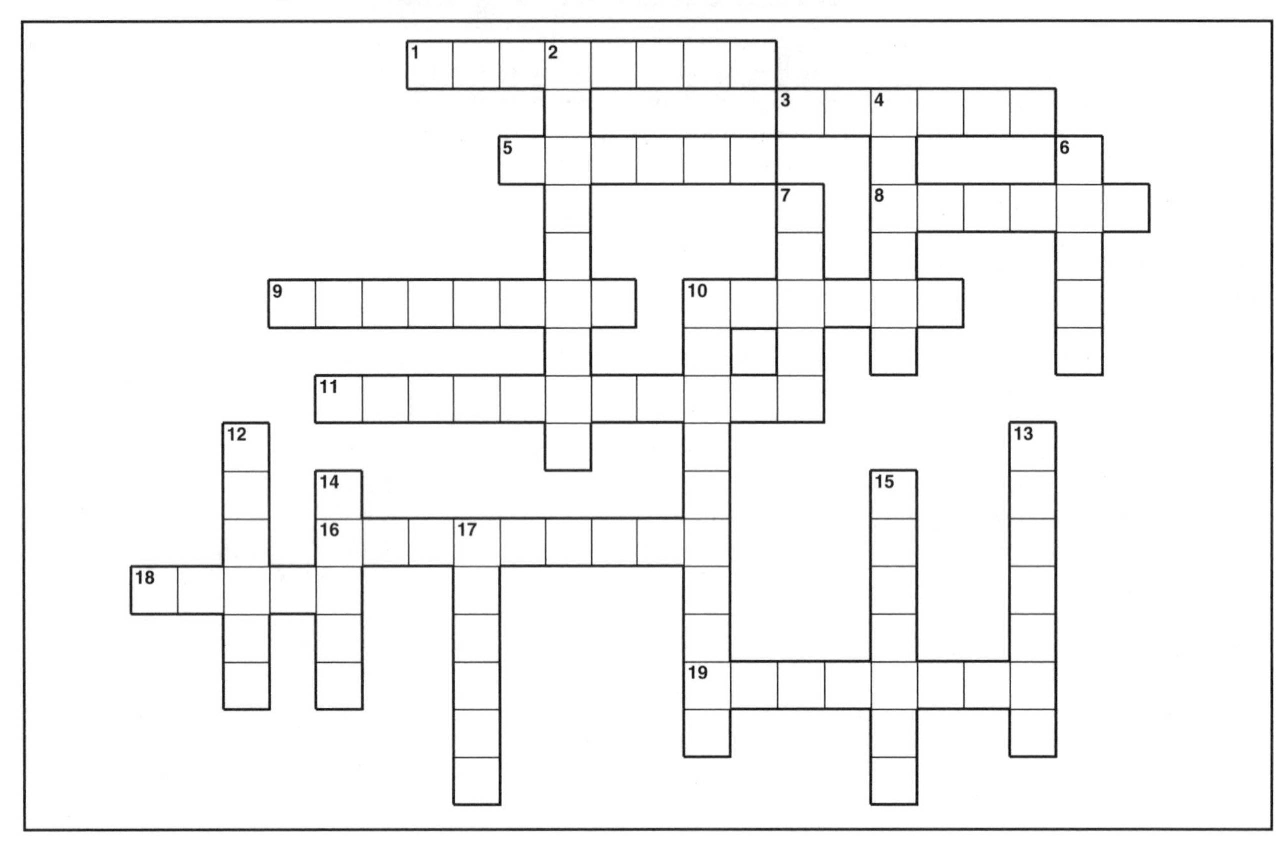

Clues for ACROSS

1 A ______ saved Angela.
3 ______ was especially lucky.
5 The V1 was a type of ______.
8 The rescuers moved ______ to free Angela.
9 The name of the family who survived.
10 The V1 did not often hit this.
11 The V1 caused this.
16 The V1 was filled with this.
18 A V1 rocket had no ______.
19 This word would not describe a V1.

Clues for DOWN

2 The nickname of the V1 rocket
4 Where Angela's parents were found
6 The house was converted into four of these.
7 This sounded an air-raid warning.
10 The name of the town where the V1 fell
12 The number of occupants of the house
13 Angela was ______ years old.
14 ______ wasn't at home when the V1 dropped.
15 People in this condition were taken to hospital.
17 The target of the V1s

Name ______________________ Date ______________

Angela's Story

Nearly eight o'clock! I was worried that I'd miss the bus and be late for school. I rushed into the bathroom to brush my teeth. Suddenly I heard a strange "put-put-putting" noise overhead. It stopped as suddenly as it had started. I think I realised that the noise meant danger, but before I could move there was a tremendous explosion and I felt a huge blast of hot air all around me. The ceiling and walls caved in, and it seemed as though the whole world was crashing down on top of me. I landed with a thud that took my breath away, and I lay there whilst everything piled up and then settled, creaking, around me. It was very dark, and my mouth and eyes were full of dust and grit.

I knew that the house had been hit by one of the new V1 rocket bombs. I couldn't understand how I was still alive. Through the darkness and dust I could see one chink of light far above me. Everything had gone quiet. I waited, and then I heard distant shouts. Although I was very cramped and sore, I screamed and shouted until I heard a voice telling me that they would dig me out in no time.

It took hours, really, with firemen, ambulancemen and air-raid wardens carefully moving the rubble of what had once been our home. At last they were able to pull me out from under the wardrobe that had protected me. I wanted my mother and father, but I was told they had already been taken to a local hospital.

No one could understand why I hadn't been killed. I had cuts, bruises and shock, but I was not seriously injured. My parents were moved from our small local hospital to a larger one. The doctors thought that my mother would have to have her crushed leg amputated, but instead they decided to rebuild it, bone by bone. My mother was in hospital for five months, and then had to have several more operations during the next few years. They tried their best to rebuild her leg, but she could never move it properly again and it caused her pain until the end of her life.

Earlier in the war, we used to complain about food rationing. We'd always had plenty of roasts, stews, eggs, cheese, fruit and vegetables, but when the war started everything changed. Each person had tokens for certain foods that were in short supply. We were only allowed a small amount of jam, cheese, butter, meat, bacon and tea, plus one egg each week. Fruit such as oranges and bananas disappeared from the shops because all the ships had to be used to carry war materials. Vegetables were the only food you could buy easily or grow yourself. I missed sweets dreadfully; these were rationed until well after the war had ended.

Clothing was also rationed. Everyone took great care of their clothes, and mothers had to cut up and alter their own clothes to fit their growing children. Spare sheets and tablecloths were turned into dresses and shirts.

After we had recovered from our injuries and found somewhere to live, we never grumbled about rationing again – we were so glad just to be alive.

Answer these questions in sentences.
Write the answers in your book.

1. What was the first clue Angela had that something unusual was about to happen?
2. Where was Angela going that day?
3. What had caused the explosion?
4. What happened to Angela as the house collapsed?
5. How do you think she felt while she was under the rubble?
6. How was she rescued?
7. Who was the most seriously injured in Angela's family?
8. How had the war changed the lives of Angela's family before they were bombed?
9. How did parents provide clothing for their growing children during the war?
10. Find the meaning of the word "rationing" in your dictionary.
11. What did Angela miss most because of rationing?
12. Using the information given in the story, make two lists in your book. Head them **Rationed** and **Not rationed**. List each of the foods the family ate during the war under the correct heading.
13. Design a poster which could have been used to encourage people to grow their own vegetables and help the war effort.

Name ______________________ Date ______________

The Solar System

This chart gives some facts about our Solar System.

Planet	Diameter (km)	Moons	Distance from sun (millions of km)	Length of day (Earth hours/ days)	Surface temperature (°C)	Orbits the sun every (Earth days/years)
Mercury	4,878	0	58	59 days	350	88 days
Venus	12,104	0	108	243 days	480	225 days
Earth	12,756	1	150	24 hours	22	365 days
Mars	6,794	2	228	24.5 hours	–23	2 years
Jupiter	142,800	16	778	10 hours	–150	12 years
Saturn	120,000	17	1,425	10.25 hours	–180	29 years
Uranus	51,800	15	2,870	15.5 hours	–210	84 years
Neptune	48,000	2	4,497	16 hours	–220	164 years
Pluto	3,000	1	5,916	6 days 9 hours	–239	248 years

Answer these questions in sentences.
Write the answers in your book.

1 Which is the biggest planet?
2 Which planets are bigger than Earth?
3 How many moons does Saturn have?
4 Why is Pluto the coldest planet?
5 Why do some planets have shorter days than Earth?
6 Which planet takes the longest time to go round the sun?
7 Which planet has the smallest diameter?
8 Why would it not be possible for us to live on Mercury?
9 Which planets have only one moon?
10 Which planet has the longest day?

Name ______________________ Date ______________

A Step Back in Time

Enter *Llewellyn House* and return to the *Victorian Age*.

As you enter Llewellyn House you leave the modern world behind and find yourself in the reign of Queen Victoria. Llewellyn House was built in 1864 and was the home of Mr. Rhys Morgan, wealthy owner of a local coalmine. Every room has been carefully furnished and decorated with genuine antique pieces. In each room, life-sized models re-create Victorian household scenes.

- In the drawing room are Mr. Morgan, his wife Carys and their children Sian (15), Daffyd (12) and Huw (10). They are listening to 14 year-old Dilys playing the piano.
- A typical family meal is laid out in the dining room, with Evans the butler polishing the cutlery.
- Mrs. Evans the cook is supervising work in the kitchen, and Ellen the kitchenmaid is washing up.
- In Mr. and Mrs. Morgan's bedroom is Megan the housemaid, filling the bowl on the washstand with hot water.
- A further two bedrooms are shared by the four older children.
- Baby Bethan is asleep in the nursery bedroom she shares with the children's nurse.
- Through an open door can be seen the playroom where Thomas (7) and Robert (5) are sitting with their nurse. Lizzie, another housemaid, is serving their tea.
- Thomas and Robert share a bedroom next door.
- An indoor toilet can be seen. Stored nearby is the portable enamel bath which is used in the bedrooms. Hot water is carried up from the kitchen.
- The top floor is the attic with five small bedrooms for the servants. There is a plain iron bedstead, a table and a cupboard in each.

Following your tour of the house you may wish to visit the old coalmine and the restored miners' cottages just beyond Brecon Fawr village. The opening times are the same as those for Llewellyn House.

Name ______________________ Date ______________

A Step Back in Time (continued)

Travel Information

Llewellyn House, Brecon Fawr, Gwent, South Wales GW6 5NT

By car
Exit the M94 at Junction 19
and follow the signs to Brecon Fawr.

By rail
Alight at Brecon station, then take the
number 7 bus to Brecon Fawr.

By bus
Take the number 606 Greenline from Cardiff.

Services and Facilities
Coffee shop and restaurant serving light meals
Picnic area
Mother and baby facilities
Wheelchair access to ground floor only

OPENING TIMES

Summer
1st April – 31st October
Open daily 10a.m. – 6p.m.

Winter
1st November – 31st March
Sundays only 10a.m. – 4 p.m.

ADMISSION

Adults	£4.00
OAPs/children (4–16 years)	£3.00
Children under 5	free
Family ticket (2 adults and 3 children)	£12.00

Answer these questions in sentences.
Write the answers in your book.

1. During whose reign was Llewellyn House built?
2. In which part of the United Kingdom is Llewellyn House?
3. How would you get to Llewellyn House if you didn't have a car?
4. How many children did Mr. and Mrs. Morgan have?
5. How many servants worked at Llewellyn House?
6. Where did the servants sleep?
7. How did Mr. Morgan earn his living?
8. How much would admission cost for Mr. Davies, Kerri (aged seven) and Matthew (aged nine)?
9. Which of the children were cared for by the nurse?
10. What is the meaning of the word "portable"?
11. How did the family get hot water for washing and bathing?
12. How could you find out what a meal would have been like in this house?
13. What could you go and see if you wanted to find out more about the local history of this time?
14. Why do you think that a visit to Llewellyn House would be a good way to find out about the Victorians?

Name ______________________ Date ______________

Megan's Story

I was only twelve when I started work up at Llewellyn House; we called it "the Big House" down in the village of Brecon Fawr.

My Mam was pleased that I was lucky enough to get the job of scullerymaid, but I didn't think so then. I'd never been away from home before, and such hard work it was. I was up at 5a.m. for a cold wash at the scullery sink, then I had to clear the grates and light the fire in the range, because the range was used for cooking and the big house was cold, even in summer. Then water had to be heated and carried up to the washstands in the bedrooms so the family could wash.

A quick breakfast of plain bread and a mug of tea was allowed before the maids served the family's breakfast. After that, the real chores began: washing up, drying dishes and pans, preparing vegetables, heating, fetching and carrying water for the laundry and keeping the kitchen scrubbed and spotless. It was an endless routine of back-breaking chores that left me exhausted. Short breaks were allowed for lunch and tea, and if there were no visitors, I might be lucky and get half an hour off in the afternoon. I was too tired to do anything other than sit by the kitchen range. Most days ended when the kitchen was spick and span after supper, usually about 10p.m., when I fell into my bed and slept.

Still, I was luckier than some. Mrs. Evans, the cook, worked me hard but she was good-hearted. Mrs. Morgan, the mistress, kept a tight hold on the pursestrings but she made sure the servants had good, plain meals such as mutton stew for lunch and bread and cheese for tea. Mrs. Evans used to treat us with leftover cakes or the occasional slice of lean ham. We could not afford food like this at home and I considered myself very lucky to eat so well.

Though the bedroom I shared with Dilys was cold, the bed was warm and comfortable and we were never beaten. Dilys was one of the housemaids and she had once been a scullerymaid at one of the other houses up the valley. The master and mistress there had been hard and the housekeeper cruel. Dilys wasn't sorry when the master died and they had to cut down on servants.

I was allowed one Sunday off every fortnight and I went to visit Mam and Da. Mrs. Evans used to send a small cake or tart with me. I earned 2/6d (12p) each week and I gave it straight to Mam to help keep the family going. Although my brother Dai was thirteen and already working down the pit, he didn't earn much. My Da was a skilled coalface worker, but sometimes he was too ill to work because of his cough, so his money wasn't regular. Mam had the three little ones to feed as well, so my money helped keep them. There had been five others apart from Dai and me, but two died of fever last year.

When I went home I couldn't help comparing our house to "the Big House". Mam and Da just had two small bedrooms for all six of them, a scullery and a living room. There was a pump for cold water and an outside lavatory. Da gets free coal which helps to keep the kitchen fire going, but with so little money coming in, Mam found it hard to feed the family. Often she would go without, so that Da and the children had enough food. It's hard to understand how some people can have so much and some can have so little.

Now life will be a bit easier. I'm fifteen and I've been given the job of housemaid, which will mean extra money. Mam and Da are proud that I'm doing so well. Now Mam wants my little sister to try for the job of scullerymaid.

Name ______________________ Date ______________

Megan's Story (continued)

Answer these questions in sentences.
Write the answers in your book.

1 Give two reasons why Megan didn't think she was lucky to get the job of scullerymaid.
2 How long was Megan's working day?
3 How long had Megan been working at Llewellyn House?
4 List six of Megan's jobs during the day.
5 What did Megan have to eat?
6 Why wasn't Dilys sorry when her previous master died?
7 How many days off did Megan get every month?
8 What did Megan's father do for a living?
9 List three differences between the house Megan's family lived in and your own.

Use a dictionary or thesaurus to find out what these words and phrases mean.

10 scullery
11 good-hearted
12 kept a tight hold on the pursestrings
13 skilled
14 regular
15 mutton
16 routine
17 chores
18 fever

Name ______________________ Date ______________

A Victorian Schoolroom

Mrs. W. Frankum
Katesgrove Victorian Schoolroom,
Elgar Road,
Reading
Berks.

Parsons Down Junior School,
Herons Way,
Thatcham,
Berkshire,
RG2 9XE
23rd. March 1996

Dear Mrs. Frankum,

Thankyou very much for arranging for Class 6P to visit you at the Victorian Schoolroom.
You must have worked very hard to collect all those slates, old books, pens, desks and other Victorian items. It was fun to dress up in Victorian clothes, especially my pinafore, but when we had to sit at those desks and be absolutely silent and still, it made us all very nervous.
When you gave us the arithmetic lesson I was worried about getting the answers wrong. Andrew was really scared when he smudged his copy writing, and you put the dunce's cap on him and made him stand in the corner. He really thought you were going to give him the cane and was very glad you only pretended to do it!
Our visit made us realise how much more enjoyable schools are today. It was a very interesting visit, but I was glad to get back!

from Sophie.

Answer these questions in sentences.
Write the answers in your book.

1 Why is Sophie writing this letter?
2 What is Mrs. Frankum's job?
3 What has Mrs. Frankum collected for the Victorian Schoolroom?
4 What did Sophie think was fun?
5 Which lessons did Sophie's class do while they were there?
6 Why was Andrew frightened?
7 What was his punishment?
8 How were the children expected to behave in the Schoolroom?
9 What did the children think about their visit?
10 Which class is Sophie in?
11 In which town is the Victorian Schoolroom?
12 Where is Sophie's school?

Name ______________________ Date ______________

A Victorian Schoolroom (continued)

13 Use Sophie's letter to solve the crossword.

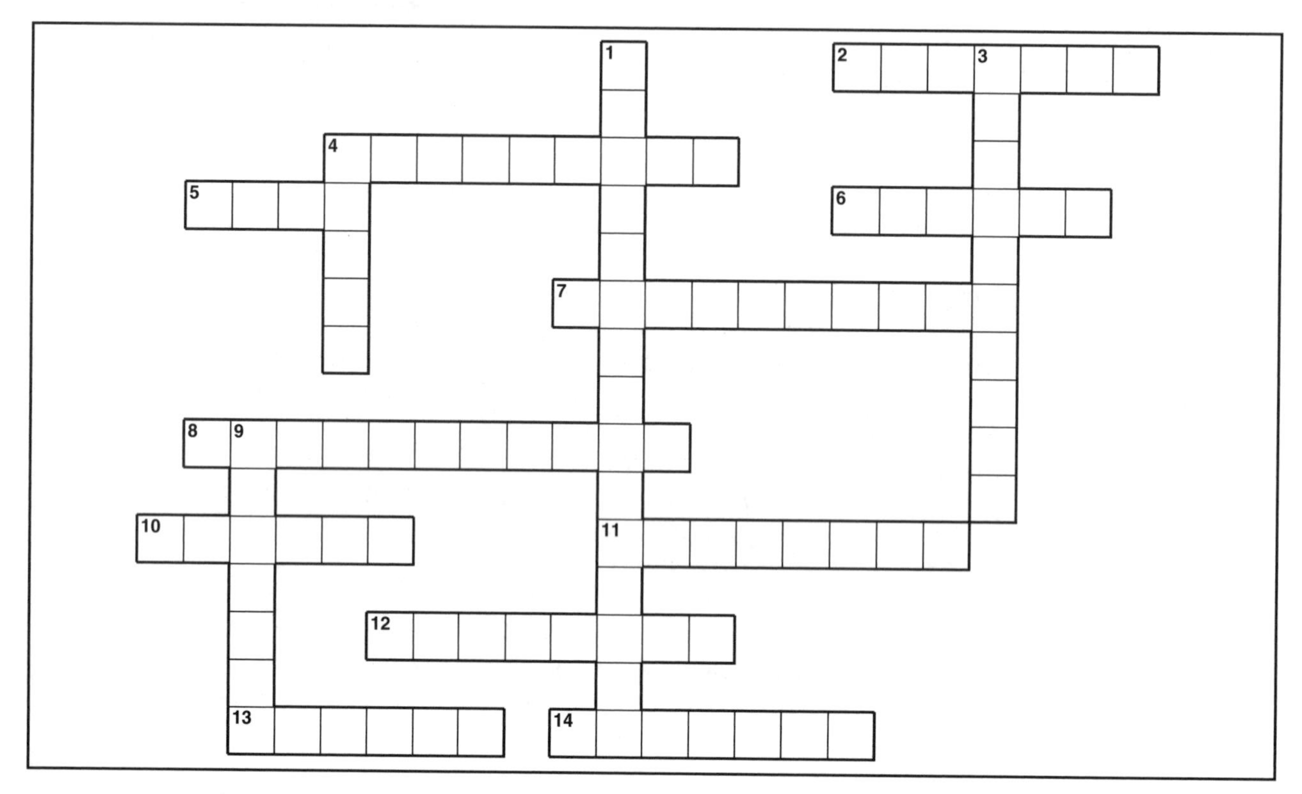

Clues for ACROSS

2 How the children felt when they arrived back at school
4 Andrew had to wear a ________ .
5 The stick that was used for punishment
6 Victorian children used to write on these.
7 The "Victorian" schoolteacher
8 The word used to describe the visit
10 Where Andrew was made to stand
11 Andrew make a smudge on this.
12 An item of clothing worn by girls at school

Clues for ACROSS (contd.)

13 The girl who wrote the letter
14 The class that made the visit

Clues for DOWN

1 The place Sophie's class visited
3 Sophie was worried during this lesson.
4 Victorian children sat at wooden ________ .
9 How the class felt when they had to sit still

Name ______________________ Date ______________

Diary of a School

School History

19th July 1897	The attendance during the week has not been good. Many children are at home, gathering fruit and others are engaged in the fields. An Attendance List was sent off today. The heat has been great today – 79 in school.
July 21st	The Wesleyan School held their treat today. Only 46 children in the mixed department came in the afternoon, and of these very few were in a fit state to stay at school, owing to the heavy storm during the break between morning and afternoon school. Registers were not marked and the children sent home. Those children who had brought their dinner might have escaped the the rain, but the bigger boys and girls went up to the Wesleyan school to watch for the other children and came back soaked. Tuesday and Thursday I was absent from school to attend examinations in London.
Aug. 2nd	Bank Holiday. School closed.
Aug. 3rd	School opened, but owing to such a small number being present, we closed again for the Harvest Vacation.
Sept. 7th	A list of absentees has been sent to the Attendance Officer on Friday Sept 10th. An increase in attendance has been the result. Some children are away from home, others at work, but the majority of the absentees are running the streets.
Sept. 14th	Mr. Tuttle, one of the school managers, visited the school.
Sept. 21st	St. Matthew's Day. Children went to church at 9.00am.
Sept. 22nd	The Sanitary Officer, Mr. Pinniger, visited the school.

From the logbook of Kintbury St. Mary's School

Answer these questions in sentences.
Write the answers in your book.

1. Do you think Kintbury was a town or a village?
2. Why was attendance not good on 19th July?
3. When was the Wesleyan School treat?
4. Why were the children not in a fit state for school on 21st July?
5. Why was the headmaster absent for two days?
6. What was special about August 2nd?
7. What does "running the streets" mean?
8. Who visited the school on 14th September?
9. Why did the children go to church on 21st September?
10. What do you think an Attendance Officer did?

Name ______________________________ Date ______________

Otter's Ransom

Winter had lost its heart. Every day the stallions Avark and Alsvid rose earlier to haul the sun's chariot across the sky, and quietly **the snow pulled back** from the valleys and plains of Midgard. Small choirs of birds sang, and Odin, Loki and Honir were eager to continue their exploration of the nine worlds.

Early one morning the three gods crossed the flaming rainbow bridge and, talking and laughing, **they spring-heeled into Midgard**. Odin and Loki had to stretch their legs to keep up with the swift Honir.

Suddenly **a late snowstorm assaulted the travellers**: thick wet flakes that tangled and danced and spun and flew in every direction until **that wild onslaught ended** as abruptly as it had begun; **the sun booming through layers of shapeless cloud**, filling it with fierce yellow light; and then there was only the orb of the sun, the **expanding acres of pale blue sky,** and **the green levels of open Midgard**.

The three gods followed the course of the river **towards its head**. And in the afternoon they walked up under a waterfall.

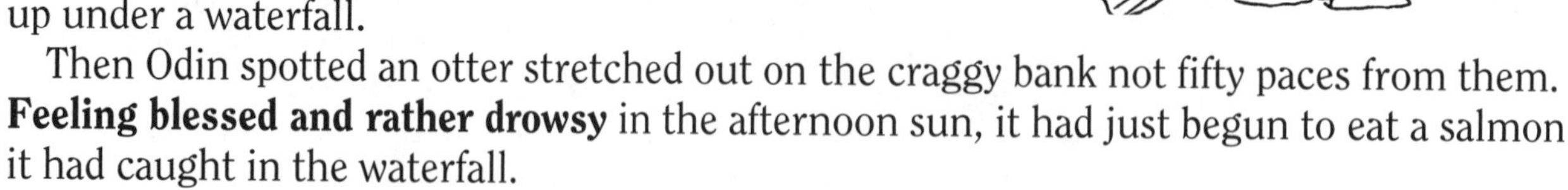

Then Odin spotted an otter stretched out on the craggy bank not fifty paces from them. **Feeling blessed and rather drowsy** in the afternoon sun, it had just begun to eat a salmon it had caught in the waterfall.

From *Norse Myths* by Kevin Crossley-Holland

In the passage, ten groups of words are in bold print.
Write each of these groups of words in your book.
Then write a sentence to explain the meaning of each group of words.
The first one has been done for you.

1. **Winter had lost its heart.**
   Winter was nearly over and spring was on its way.
2. **the snow pulled back**
3. **they spring-heeled into Midgard**
4. **a late snowstorm assaulted the travellers**
5. **that wild onslaught ended**
6. **the sun booming through layers of shapeless cloud**
7. **expanding acres of pale blue sky**
8. **the green levels of open Midgard**
9. **towards its head**
10. **Feeling blessed and rather drowsy**

Name ______________________ Date ______________

Fun in the Sun!

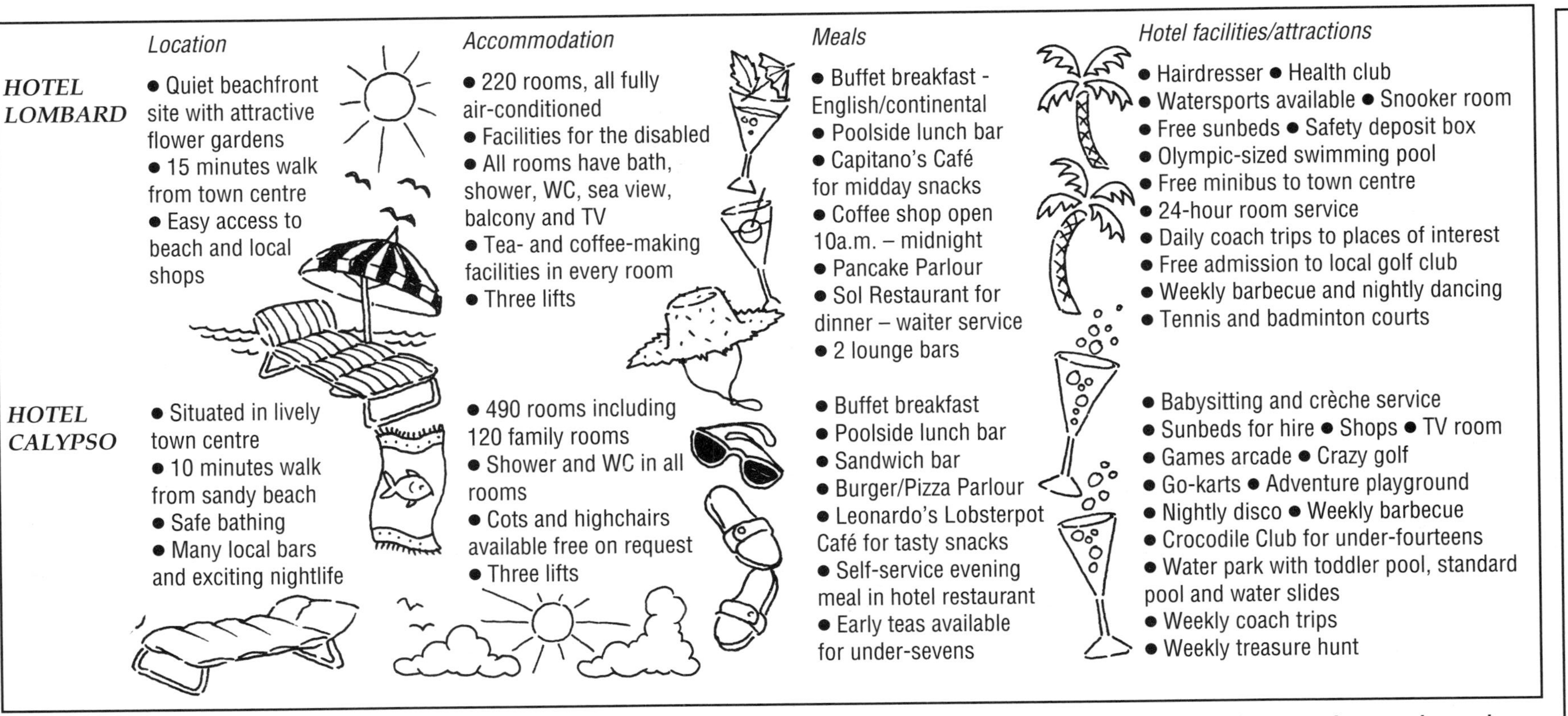

	Location	Accommodation	Meals	Hotel facilities/attractions
HOTEL LOMBARD	• Quiet beachfront site with attractive flower gardens • 15 minutes walk from town centre • Easy access to beach and local shops	• 220 rooms, all fully air-conditioned • Facilities for the disabled • All rooms have bath, shower, WC, sea view, balcony and TV • Tea- and coffee-making facilities in every room • Three lifts	• Buffet breakfast - English/continental • Poolside lunch bar • Capitano's Café for midday snacks • Coffee shop open 10a.m. – midnight • Pancake Parlour • Sol Restaurant for dinner – waiter service • 2 lounge bars	• Hairdresser • Health club • Watersports available • Snooker room • Free sunbeds • Safety deposit box • Olympic-sized swimming pool • Free minibus to town centre • 24-hour room service • Daily coach trips to places of interest • Free admission to local golf club • Weekly barbecue and nightly dancing • Tennis and badminton courts
HOTEL CALYPSO	• Situated in lively town centre • 10 minutes walk from sandy beach • Safe bathing • Many local bars and exciting nightlife	• 490 rooms including 120 family rooms • Shower and WC in all rooms • Cots and highchairs available free on request • Three lifts	• Buffet breakfast • Poolside lunch bar • Sandwich bar • Burger/Pizza Parlour • Leonardo's Lobsterpot Café for tasty snacks • Self-service evening meal in hotel restaurant • Early teas available for under-sevens	• Babysitting and crèche service • Sunbeds for hire • Shops • TV room • Games arcade • Crazy golf • Go-karts • Adventure playground • Nightly disco • Weekly barbecue • Crocodile Club for under-fourteens • Water park with toddler pool, standard pool and water slides • Weekly coach trips • Weekly treasure hunt

This information sheet gives details of the Hotel Lombard and the Hotel Calypso. These hotels are situated on the Costa del Sol in Spain. It is a popular resort, providing sun, sea and sand for thousands of holidaymakers every year.

Answer the following questions in sentences. Write the answers in your book.

1 Which hotel would be better for families with children?
2 Give three reasons.
3 List three things that are the same in both hotels
4 Which restaurant in which hotel offers waiter service?
5 Which hotel has more places to eat?
6 Which hotel lies outside the town centre?
7 Name a facility which is free in Hotel Lombard but not at the Calypso.
8 Which extra feature do all the rooms have in the Hotel Lombard?
9 At which hotel would you prefer to stay? Give three reasons.
10 Design an advert on A4 paper for the hotel of your choice.

Name ______________________ Date ______________

Dick Turpin

"Stand and deliver: your money or your life!"

These orders were shouted to the terrified passengers on the London to Bath stagecoach. The women clung to their menfolk who were powerless to prevent the theft of their money and other valuables, unless they were foolhardy enough to risk a bullet. As the masked highwayman snatched his loot, the noise of fast-approaching hoofbeats announced the arrival of a contingent of the King's men, too late to prevent the robbery, but in time to chase that most notorious of highwaymen – Dick Turpin.

His heart lurched with fear as the exhausted horse beneath him stumbled and all but fell. It was his skill as a horseman and his grim determination to escape that enabled him to check the fall, rein in, and speed off again towards the town, away from his pursuers.

Once he had left the open countryside and heathland behind him, he could make for the disused barn on the outskirts of the town, bed down his horse, and then mingle with the townsfolk before finding a safe place for the night, perhaps with a friend.

But friends were few and far between for a hunted man such as Dick Turpin. His parents were innkeepers who had found young Dick a wayward boy. As he grew up, it was clear that no ordinary day's work would keep him occupied. He first enjoyed the excitement of cattle stealing, and then the greater challenge of highway robbery.

Now Dick Turpin was fleeing after a particularly daring robbery at one of his favourite ambush locations – a small copse on Hounslow Heath. It was difficult for him to believe that stagecoach passengers travelling from London to Bath still risked taking money and jewellery on the journey, despite the danger from men such as him. He knew that some people secretly admired his nerve in committing his robberies and his skill in evading capture by the authorities. Other people, however, lived in terror and regarded him as a vicious criminal.

In 1739 he paid the price for his crimes, when he was captured and hanged at York. He was aged only 33 – one of the most famous English lawbreakers of all time.

Find a word in the box which means the same as each of these words.

1 **powerless**
2 **contingent**
3 **notorious**
4 **lurched**
5 **outskirts**
6 **mingle**
7 **wayward**
8 **apparently**
9 **occupied**
10 **evade**
11 **locations**
12 **eventually**
13 **daring**

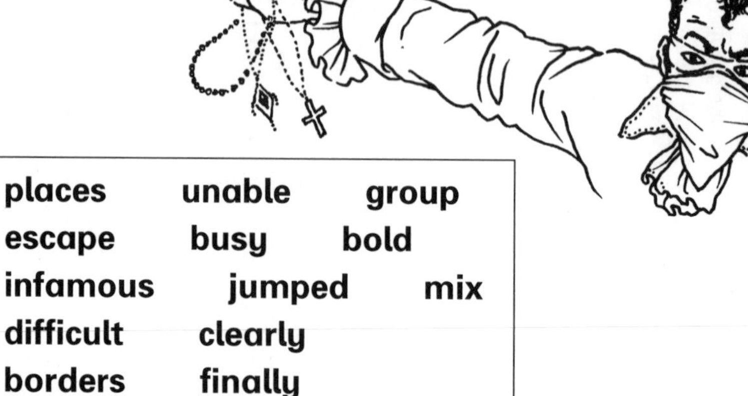

places	**unable**	**group**
escape	**busy**	**bold**
infamous	**jumped**	**mix**
difficult	**clearly**	
borders	**finally**	

Answer these questions in sentences.
Write the answers in your book.

14 How do you know that Dick Turpin was afraid?
15 Where had the robbery taken place?
16 What were the surroundings like at the point where he had held up the coach?
17 Why were the passengers frightened of standing up to him?
18 Where were the travellers going?
19 Why had Dick Turpin so few friends?
20 What were the two main reasons that enabled him to escape?
21 Why do you think that some people admired him?

Name ______________________ Date ______________

The Alchymist's Cat

It is the winter of 1664, and Imelza the cat is out hunting...

Harry shuffled out of the straw and shielded his tiny eyes from the bright moon. What a glorious night for pilfering and eating your fill! The rat thrashed his tail gleefully and hopped on to the cobbles. He did not hear her spring.

"Aaaarrrggghhh!" he bawled, when he became aware of her hot breath on his neck and felt her strong claws squeeze round him.

"I'm dead, Bert!" he wailed. "Flee, while you can..." and then he was silent. The cat trotted away contented, with the dead, juicy rat dangling from her mouth.

She wanted to enjoy this delicacy in peace and she knew the very spot. On to a rain barrel she leapt, and from there jumped to a windowsill. Then she surefootedly walked around the side of the building, using one of the decorative beams set into the wall as a ledge. And so up to the sloping roof, where she stretched herself out on the cool tiles and devoured her supper.

In the full glare of the moon she was a gorgeous creature; her ginger fur almost seemed to glow under its baleful beams. Her features were fine and delicate, having a sharp chin and a small pink nose – indeed she was considered a great beauty, yet none of her countless suitors had claimed her.

From her vantage point she surveyed London like an empress with a supreme look of disdain on her proud face. The streets were quiet now; even the dog had ceased howling. All was calm. Yet she was wise enough to know that it was on such nights as these that the most gruesome murders were committed or the direst tragedies could occur. Death and disaster were always eager visitors when they were least expected.

A man trailed through the streets below with a lantern in his hand. With her glittering eyes she watched his progress and saw him pause on every corner where he called out, "Eleven of the clock on a fine October night and all's well."

She hated mankind – they were ugly, stupid and cruel beasts – yet she had wit to use them on occasion. There were at least seven houses in the city where she was known and where a spot of milk or table scraps could be had in return for a measure of play acting. A smile spread over her face as she thought how easy it was to mew prettily and press her head against their shambling legs in a mock display of affection.

From *The Alchymist's Cat* by Robin Jarvis

Name ______________________________ Date ______________

The Alchymist's Cat (continued)

1 Match each of the words in list **A** to the word with the closest meaning in list **B**.

A	B
shielded	**worst**
pilfering	**ate**
thrashed	**stealing**
spring	**shaded**
flee	**jump**
dangling	**watched**
delicacy	**stopped**
devoured	**treat**
surveyed	**hanging**
ceased	**escape**
direst	**wriggled**

Answer these questions in sentences.
Write the answers in your book.

2 What were Harry's plans that night?
3 What spoiled Harry's plans for the night?
4 Why did the cat want to find a quiet spot?
5 How did she get to it?
6 Why could the cat be clearly seen?
7 What did the cat look like?
8 What did the cat do after she had eaten the rat?
9 What could happen on such a quiet night?
10 Who did the cat see?
11 What season was it?
12 What did the cat think of human beings?
13 Why did the cat pretend to like human beings?
14 What was the atmosphere like in the streets?
15 What was the cat thinking before she saw the man?